The Curious Case of Benjamin Button & Other Stories

LEVEL THREE   1000 HEADWORDS

OXFORD
UNIVERSITY PRESS

Great Clarendon Street, Oxford, ox2 6dp, United Kingdom

Oxford University Press is a department of the University of Oxford.
It furthers the University's objective of excellence in research, scholarship,
and education by publishing worldwide. Oxford is a registered trade
mark of Oxford University Press in the UK and in certain other countries

This edition © Oxford University Press 2016

The moral rights of the author have been asserted

First published in Dominoes 2011

2025 2024 2023

22

ISBN: 978 0 19 424927 0   Book
ISBN: 978 0 19 463974 3   Book and Audio Pack
Audio not available separately

Printed in China

This book is printed on paper from certified and well-managed sources

ACKNOWLEDGEMENTS

Text adaptation by: Clare West

Illustrations by: Nick Hardcastle

Cover image by: PunchStock (man & clocks/Brand X Pictures)

The publisher would like to thank the following for permission to reproduce photographs:
Alamy pp. 74 (Pictorial Press), 75 (Victor Watts), 76 (Edith Nesbit/Mary Evans Picture
Library, Joseph Conrad/INTERFOTO); Getty Images pp. 36 (Bettmann), 45 (Sasha/Stringer/
Hulton Archive), 76 (Jack London/Universal History Archive/Universal Images Group,
O. Henry/Hulton Archive/Stringer); iStockphoto p. 28 (bowl/Kyoshino).

DOMINOES

Series Editors: Bill Bowler and Sue Parminter

The Curious Case of Benjamin Button & Other Stories

F. Scott Fitzgerald

Text adaptation by Clare West

Illustrated by Nick Hardcastle

Francis Scott Key Fitzgerald was born in St Paul, Minnesota, USA, in 1896. He studied at Princeton University in New Jersey, where he started writing. He published his first novel *This Side of Paradise* in 1920 and married his wife, Zelda, soon afterwards. He published two more novels in the 1920s – *The Beautiful and Damned* (1922) and *The Great Gatsby* (1925) – and became a famous American writer of the Jazz Age because of them. Zelda and Scott separated in 1931. In the 1930s Fitzgerald published many magazine stories and also worked as a Hollywood scriptwriter. He published one more novel, *Tender is the Night*, in 1934 and left one last novel, *The Last Tycoon*, unfinished at the time of his death in 1940. It was published in 1941.

OXFORD
UNIVERSITY PRESS

BEFORE READING

1 **What are the seven stories in this book about? Match the sentences with the pictures. Look ahead in the book to help you.**

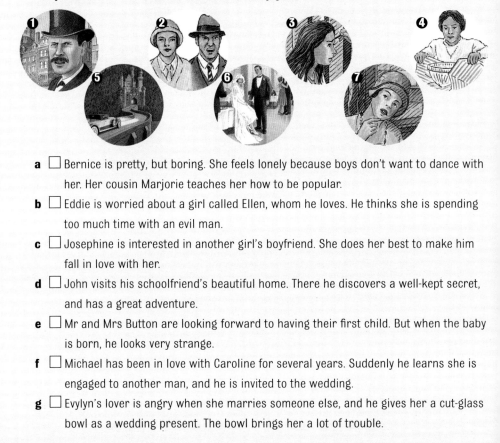

a ☐ Bernice is pretty, but boring. She feels lonely because boys don't want to dance with her. Her cousin Marjorie teaches her how to be popular.

b ☐ Eddie is worried about a girl called Ellen, whom he loves. He thinks she is spending too much time with an evil man.

c ☐ Josephine is interested in another girl's boyfriend. She does her best to make him fall in love with her.

d ☐ John visits his schoolfriend's beautiful home. There he discovers a well-kept secret, and has a great adventure.

e ☐ Mr and Mrs Button are looking forward to having their first child. But when the baby is born, he looks very strange.

f ☐ Michael has been in love with Caroline for several years. Suddenly he learns she is engaged to another man, and he is invited to the wedding.

g ☐ Evylyn's lover is angry when she marries someone else, and he gives her a cut-glass bowl as a wedding present. The bowl brings her a lot of trouble.

2 **Which sentences about US life in the early 1900s are true? Correct the false ones.**

a Most women and girls had long hair.

b People used cars for travelling a long way over land.

c Most men brought home all the money for their families' needs.

d The best way to send a very quick message was by telephone.

e Many women smoked cigarettes.

f Rich people had servants to cook and clean for them at home.

The Curious Case of Benjamin Button

❧ Part 1 ❧

In 1860, Roger Button and his wife were living in Baltimore, USA. Mrs Button was in hospital, waiting to have her first baby. Mr Button hoped they would have a son, because he wanted to send him to Yale, one of the two most important **colleges** in the United States (Harvard is the other). He himself had studied at Yale.

On the morning the baby was **expected** to arrive, Mr Button got up early and hurried to the hospital. As he arrived, he saw Dr Keene, their family doctor, leaving.

'Dr Keene!' Mr Button called. 'Oh, Dr Keene!'

The doctor turned and looked strangely at him.

'What happened?' asked Mr Button excitedly. 'Is it a boy? How is my wife? Tell me! Is the child born?'

Dr Keene said darkly, 'Well, you could say the child is born – in a way.' He gave Mr Button another strange look.

'Is it a boy or a girl?'

'Now look here!' cried Dr Keene, suddenly very angry. 'Go and see for yourself. It's most **curious**. I've never seen a **case** like it. And it's too bad! What about my good name as a doctor? You didn't think of that, did you?'

college a place where students go to study when they finish high school

expect to think that something will happen

curious strange

case example

1

'What's the matter?' asked Mr Button, by now very worried.

'Go and see! And find yourself another doctor. I'm finished with you!' He turned and walked away very fast.

Mr Button could not think what had happened. He slowly went into the hospital, and spoke to the first nurse he met.

'Good morning,' he said. 'I – I am Mr Button.'

The girl gave a frightened scream. 'Upstairs!' she cried, showing him the stairs. 'Go – go up!'

Mr Button went upstairs, where he met another nurse.

'I'm Mr Button,' he said. 'I – I want to see my child.'

The nurse looked at him in **disgust**. 'Come with me, Mr Button,' she said, and took him to a large room with a number of new-born babies, each in its small **cot**.

'Well, which is mine?' asked Mr Button.

'There!' said the nurse, showing him one of the cots.

An old man, who looked about seventy years old, was sitting in a cot which was much too small for him. He had a large, white blanket round him. His thin hair was almost white and he had a long, grey beard.

'Am I crazy?' shouted Mr Button angrily. 'Or are you playing some kind of game with me?'

'It doesn't seem like a game to us,' said the nurse crossly, 'But I can promise you, that's your child.'

Mr Button hid his face in his hands. 'What will people say?' he whispered. 'What must I do?'

'You must take him home,' said the nurse, 'Immediately!'

Suddenly the old man said, in a thin, high voice, 'Look here, if you think I'm going to walk home in this blanket, you're making a big mistake. And the clothes they've got for me here, well, they're much too small!'

'What shall I do?' Mr Button asked the nurse.

disgust a strong feeling of dislike

cot a small bed for a baby, with high sides

'Go and buy your son some clothes,' she replied.

It was difficult for Mr Button to find the right thing. Babies' clothes were too small and boys' clothes were not suitable for a baby. In the end, he bought a **fancy dress** boy's suit, and ran back to the hospital with it.

The old man took one look at it and said, 'I don't want people to laugh at me.'

'Well, they're going to laugh at *me*!' replied Mr Button angrily. 'Now put it on at once, or there'll be trouble!'

'All right, Father, you know best. Just as you say.'

The sound of the word 'Father' suddenly gave Mr Button a really unpleasant surprise. Was this man, with his grey beard, his watery eyes and his old, yellow teeth really his baby son?

During the next few days, Mr Button had his son's beard **shaved** off, his hair **dyed** an unnatural black, and clothes made specially for him. Mr Button bought all kinds of **toys**, ordering his son to play with them, although it was clear that the old man was not really interested.

When people in Baltimore heard about Benjamin, they talked about nothing else for months. Benjamin himself was as **puzzled** as everyone else. 'Why do I look and feel so old?' he wondered. He spent most of his time at home, reading books and secretly smoking his father's **cigars**.

fancy dress party clothes that you wear to look like a character

shave to cut the hair on a man's face

dye to change the colour of something; something that changes the colour of things

toy something that a child plays with

puzzled when you can't understand something

cigar a thick, brown cigarette

By the time he was twelve years old, he still looked old. But one day, Benjamin looked in his mirror and discovered that under the dye his hair was grey, not white, and that his skin looked healthier.

When he was eighteen, he had a straight back like a man of fifty; he had more hair and it was dark grey. So his father made him take the **examination** to enter Yale College, and Benjamin was accepted. He was invited to see Mr Hart, the **registrar**.

'Good morning,' said Mr Hart. 'You've come to discuss your son, I suppose.'

'No,' said Benjamin. '*I'm* Benjamin Button.'

'Now, Mr Button, you don't expect me to think that's true!'

Benjamin gave a tired smile. 'I'm eighteen,' he said.

The registrar pointed angrily at the door. 'Get out of here!' he said. 'You're crazy and dangerous!'

Benjamin left the office. On his miserable walk to the train station, he was followed by a large crowd of college students. They laughed and shouted at him.

'Call yourself eighteen! You're more like fifty!'

'This isn't an old people's home, you know!'

'Go to Harvard, why don't you!'

Benjamin walked faster, and soon he was running. 'I'll show them!' he thought. 'I *will* go to Harvard, and then they'll be sorry!' Safely on the train for Baltimore, he put his head out of the window. 'You'll be sorry for this!' he shouted.

'Ha-ha!' the students laughed. 'Ha-ha-ha!' It was the biggest mistake that Yale College ever made ...

In 1880 Benjamin was twenty, and he went to work in his father's business. That year, his father took him to several fashionable dances. Roger was now fifty, and he and his son looked just like brothers.

examination a paper with many questions to see how much you know

registrar the college officer who keeps information about the students

4

One night in August, they drove to a dance at a country house. It was a lovely evening, with a full moon. Just as they arrived, they saw a family getting out of a **carriage** – a lady, an older man, then a beautiful young woman. As soon as Benjamin saw her, his heart suddenly began to beat loudly. It was first love.

The evening seemed awfully long to Benjamin until it was time for his dance with the young lady, Hildegarde Moncrief. But when the moment came, and he held her in his arms, he felt that his life was just beginning.

'I like older men,' she told him. 'Young boys are so stupid. They tell me how much they drink at college, and how much money they lose when they play cards. I think it's better for me to marry a man of fifty who'll take care of me, than to marry a man of thirty and take care of *him*.'

Six months later, the people of Baltimore heard the surprising news that Hildegarde Moncrief was **engaged** to marry Benjamin Button. Her worried father told everyone, 'It's terrible for a lovely girl like my daughter to throw herself into the arms of a fifty-year-old!' People asked each other, 'Is she really going to marry Benjamin? And if she does, will they be happy together?'

carriage an old kind of car that horses pull

engaged when two people agree that they are going to marry

READING CHECK

1 Put these sentences in the correct order. Number them 1–9.

a ☐ Roger learns that the old man is his baby son.

b ☐ Hildegarde agrees to marry Benjamin.

c ☐ The nurse shows Roger an old man sitting in a cot.

d ☐ The Button family's doctor speaks angrily to Roger.

e ☐ At eighteen, Benjamin tries to enter Yale College.

f ☐ Benjamin falls wildly in love with Hildegarde Moncrief.

g ☐ Roger Button hurries to the hospital to see his baby.

h ☐ At twenty, Benjamin starts working for his father.

i ☐ Benjamin finds being a child is hard because he looks and feels so old.

2 Match the sentences with the people.

Benjamin

Hildegarde

Roger Button

Mr Moncrief

Dr Keene

Mr Hart

a . .Dr. Keene. . doesn't want to help the Button family any more.

b . . . . has to buy special clothes for his son.

c People in Baltimore talk about . . . . for months.

d . . . . the registrar, doesn't want a fifty-year-old student at Yale.

e Surprisingly, ... likes older men better than young ones.

f . . . . is worried about his daughter's future.

6

ACTIVITIES

WORD WORK

1 Correct the boxed words in these sentences. They are all words from Part 1 of *The Curious Case of Benjamin Button*.

a Dr Keene says that it is all most furious . .... *curious*....

b Everybody thinks that it is an unusual chase . ...

c There are lots of boys for Benjamin to play with at home. ....

d Benjamin watches Hildegarde step out of her damage . ...

2 Use the words in the baby clothes to complete the sentences.

| expected | dyed | cigars | examination | college | cot |
| engaged | shaved | puzzled | registrar | disgusted | fancy dress |

a The nurses were . *disgusted*. . when they saw the baby, but Roger still had hopes of sending his son to his old .... *college*.... one day.

b Benjamin was taken out of his .... and was given some ....
clothes to wear.

c His beard was .... off, and his hair was ....

d He often looked .... , and sometimes smoked his father's ....

e Later, he passed the .... to enter Yale, and went to see the ....

f He never .... a girl as pretty as Hildegarde to love him, but soon they were ....

GUESS WHAT

What happens to Benjamin Button in the last part of the story? Tick three boxes.

a ☐ He marries Hildegarde.

b ☐ He falls in love with someone else.

c ☐ He and his wife are happy all their lives.

d ☐ He goes to study at Harvard.

e ☐ He goes to war, and fights for his country.

f ☐ He dies as a very old man.

The Curious Case of Benjamin Button

Part 2

Hildegarde married Benjamin, and at first they were very happy. As the manager of his father's business, Benjamin made a lot of money. Soon the people of Baltimore stopped whispering about the way he looked, and even Hildegarde's parents accepted him.

By 1895 Benjamin was really enjoying life. He owned a large, comfortable house, and he was also the first man in Baltimore to own a car.

'He seems to grow younger every year,' his friends used to say. They wished they looked half as healthy as he did.

There was only one thing that worried Benjamin. His wife did not **attract** him any more. She was now a woman of thirty-five, with a fourteen-year-old son called Roscoe. As the years passed, her bright hair became a boring brown, and she showed no interest in going to parties or dances. 'The sad fact is, she's getting older,' Benjamin said to himself. He felt more and more unhappy at home.

At the beginning of the Spanish-American **War** in 1898, Benjamin joined the army and was away from Baltimore for three years. He loved the exciting life he led in the army, but he had to return to manage his business.

attract to make someone interested in you, or love you

war fighting between countries or people

8

When he arrived home, he was **shocked** to discover how much older Hildegarde looked. He himself looked like a young man of thirty. For a moment he was frightened. 'What will happen to me in the future?' he wondered. 'How can I go on getting younger?'

His wife was angry with him. 'Why do you try to look so young?' she asked him crossly. 'You could stop it, you know!'

'But Hildegarde, I can't help it!'

'You just want to be different from other people,' she replied. 'Well, that's up to you!'

And from then on, they did not spend much time together.

To make matters worse, he found that he enjoyed going out and meeting new people more than ever. He was at all the Baltimore parties, talking to the prettiest young women and making them laugh, while his wife sat with the old ladies, looking at him with sad, puzzled eyes.

'Look!' the other guests used to say. 'That poor young man, tied to a woman of forty-five. He must be twenty years younger than her!' They forgot what their parents had said about these same two people, back in 1880: 'Look at that lovely young girl! She shouldn't marry a man who's so much older than her!'

Benjamin tried not to think about his growing unhappiness at home. He had many new interests to keep him busy. He started playing **golf**, and he learnt all the newest dances; every young man in town wished he could play golf and dance as well as Benjamin.

Because he went out so often, he found that he was spending less and less time at the office. But he said to himself, 'I've worked hard in this business for twenty-five years. Now it's time to hand it over to young Roscoe. Then I'll really be able to enjoy myself!' His son Roscoe had recently **graduated** from Harvard. He looked very like Benjamin, and people often **mistook them for each other**.

One September day in 1910, a man who looked about twenty

shocked very surprised by something bad

golf a game where you hit a ball into a number of holes

graduate to finish your studies at college or university

mistake someone for somebody to think that a person is someone different

years old was accepted as a first-year student at Harvard University. He did not tell the registrar that he would never see fifty again, or that his son had graduated ten years before. He started studying, and did well in his class.

But his greatest success was on the football field. He was chosen to play for his university, and in the game against Yale he played better than anyone else, and with a cold, hard anger. He was the reason why Yale was beaten so badly, and why eleven Yale players were carried **unconscious** from the field. All that year, he was the most famous man at Harvard.

The next year he played for Harvard again, although everyone said he seemed smaller. The following year, he wasn't strong enough to be chosen. He looked about sixteen years old.

When he graduated in 1914, he went home to Baltimore. Hildegarde was now living in Italy, so he went to live with Roscoe. He did not get a very **enthusiastic** welcome. Roscoe was now married and an important person in Baltimore, so he did not want people to talk about his surprisingly young-looking father.

In 1920, Roscoe's first child was born. There was a little boy, who seemed about ten years old, living in the house at the time. Nobody explained that he was the new baby's grandfather.

unconscious
sleeping because you are ill or something hit you

enthusiastic
feeling or showing a lot of interest in something

Five years later, Roscoe took his own son and little Benjamin to the **kindergarten** together. Benjamin had a very happy year or two there, but then he began to feel afraid of the other boys because they were bigger. He was taken away from the kindergarten as Roscoe's son moved up to the next class.

Now his **nursemaid**, Nana, became the centre of his little world. On sunny days they walked in the park, and on wet days they played games indoors. At the end of the long day, at five o'clock, he used to go upstairs with Nana and eat baby food with a spoon. The past did not enter his untroubled childish sleep: he did not remember his young wife whom he had loved, or his time fighting bravely for his country, or his days playing football at college, or the parties where he broke so many girls' hearts. There were only the white, safe walls of his cot, and Nana, and a man who came to see him

sometimes, and a great orange ball that Nana called 'sun'. He remembered nothing. When he was hungry for his milk, he cried, and that was all.

And then his white cot, and the faces that moved above him, and the warm sweet smell of his milk, disappeared – and it was all dark.

kindergarten a class to prepare young children for school

nursemaid a woman who takes care of a young child at home

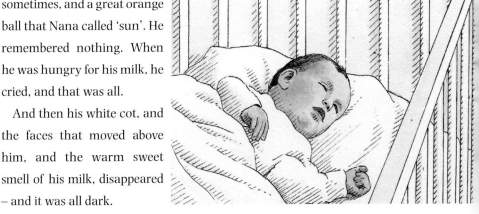

READING CHECK

1 Are these sentences about Benjamin Button true or false? Tick the boxes.

	True	False
a His father's business doesn't make much money.	☐	☑
b He is the first man in Baltimore to own a car.	☐	☐
c He seems to grow older every year.	☐	☐
d His wife is angry about the way he looks.	☐	☐
e He can't play golf or dance well.	☐	☐
f In 1910, he enters Harvard University.	☐	☐
g He goes to kindergarten with his grandson.	☐	☐
h He becomes a baby, and dies.	☐	☐

2 Correct the mistakes in these sentences.

parents

a Hildegarde's ~~sisters~~ accept Benjamin.

b Benjamin and Hildegarde have a daughter.

c Benjamin fights in the First World War.

d He is away from home for five years.

e He spends a lot of time at parties talking to old ladies.

f He hands over the business to his brother.

g Benjamin is very pleased to beat the Yale tennis team.

h His wife moves away and lives in Spain.

i Benjamin's mother becomes the centre of his world.

WORD WORK

Match words in Part 2 of *The Curious Case of Benjamin Button* with these definitions.

a fighting between countries or people w _ar_

b very surprised by something bad s _ _ _ _ _ _

c a game where you hit a ball with a stick into a number of holes g _ _ _

d sleeping because you are ill or something hit you u _ _ _ _ _ _ _ _ _ _

e feeling or showing a lot of interest in something e _ _ _ _ _ _ _ _ _ _ _

f to make someone interested in you, or love you a _ _ _ _ _ _

g a class to prepare young children for school k _ _ _ _ _ _ _ _ _ _ _

h a woman who takes care of a young child at home n _ _ _ _ _ _ _ _

i to finish your studies at college or university g _ _ _ _ _ _ _

j to think that a person is someone different
   m _ _ _ _ _ _ s _ _ _ _ _ _ _ f _ _ s _ _ _ _ _ _ _

GUESS WHAT

The next story is called *Bernice Bobs Her Hair*. What do you think happens in it? Tick two boxes.

Bernice...

a ☐ gets angry with someone, and stops being their friend.

b ☐ has her hair cut short, which shocks some people.

c ☐ loses her hair after an illness, but it grows back.

d ☐ suddenly becomes very popular after she dyes her hair.

e ☐ needs money. So she cuts her hair and sells it.

f ☐ teaches someone a lesson.

Bernice Bobs Her Hair

There was a Saturday evening dance at the **country club**, and Warren McIntyre was there. He was a student at Yale, and had come home for the summer holidays. It was hot inside, so he went out into the cool night air for a cigarette.

He was thinking about Marjorie Harvey. What a girl! With her beauty and her quick, clever tongue, she was popular with everybody. Warren had been crazy about her for a long time. But one day she had told him, 'I'm sorry, Warren, I don't love you. You see, when I'm away from you, I forget you and go out with other boys. So I know I don't love you.'

Marjorie had been away very often this summer, and each time she came home, there were a lot of letters for her on the Harveys' hall table. 'These letters must be from the boys she's met!' thought Warren miserably.

And now it was August already, and he still couldn't spend time alone with Marjorie, because her **cousin** Bernice was visiting her for a month. If he wanted to be with Marjorie, he always had to find a boy for Bernice, and that wasn't easy. Everyone agreed that, although Bernice was pretty, she was no fun at a party. She had nothing interesting to say.

When the two cousins reached Marjorie's house that night, they said goodnight and went to their own bedrooms.

As she brushed her teeth, Bernice wondered for the hundredth time why she wasn't as popular as the other girls. She decided to talk to Marjorie's mother before going to bed, and walked down the hall to her aunt's bedroom. Through the partly open door she heard her own name, and stopped to listen.

'She's hopeless!' Marjorie was saying. 'I know she's pretty and sweet and she can cook, but that's not enough! Men don't like her, and that's what matters.'

country club a club in the country where people go to meet other people

cousin the son (or daughter) of your father's (or mother's) brother (or sister)

'I think you ought to be able to do something for her,' Mrs Harvey said. 'I know her conversation isn't very exciting.'

'Exciting!' cried Marjorie. 'All she can say to a boy is that it's hot or the floor is crowded or she's going to school in New York next year. No, Mother, I've done my best. I've been polite and I've made men dance with her, but they really don't want to be bored. I've even tried to tell her about clothes and things, but she just looks strangely at me. These days it's every girl for herself. I can't help her any more.'

'Go to bed, you silly child,' laughed Mrs Harvey.

'Oh well, goodnight then, Mother,' said Marjorie. When she came out of the bedroom, the hall was empty.

At breakfast next morning Bernice said to Marjorie, 'I heard what you said about me to your mother last night.'

Marjorie looked up, surprised, but said nothing.

'I suppose I should go home if I'm stopping you enjoying yourself. I've tried to be nice, but *you* haven't been nice to *me*. And your friends don't like me.' Bernice was almost crying.

After a short silence Marjorie said, 'When do you want to go?'

'Go!' Bernice repeated in a shocked voice.

'Didn't you say you were going? Oh, you were only **bluffing**!'

bluff to try to make somebody think that you will do something

15

Bernice started crying loudly, while Marjorie looked bored.

'If I g-g-go home early,' cried Bernice, her face wet, 'My m-m-mother will know and she'll w-wonder–'

'I'll give you some money,' said Marjorie coldly, 'And you can spend this last week anywhere you want. There's a very nice hotel–'

Bernice ran wildly out of the room, and did not come to the **dining room** for lunch. But later that day, Marjorie found Bernice waiting for her in her bedroom.

'I've decided,' she said tearfully, 'that maybe you're right. I'm ready to do whatever you say, to make myself more – more interesting.'

'All right then. Let's start with your **eyebrows**. You should brush them, to make them look better. And when you go home, you must have your teeth straightened.'

'What else?' said Bernice, a little shocked at her cousin's honesty.

'Oh, I'm just beginning! You shouldn't stand so straight when you dance. If you're tall, that makes it harder for the man, and he's the one that matters.'

'Go on.' Bernice was finding all this difficult to accept.

'You've got to learn to be nice to the sad birds – that's what I call them – the men who aren't good-looking or popular. They're a large part of any crowd. Every girl needs them, because if you dance with the sad birds and keep them happy, they'll want to dance with you again. Then the good-looking boys will notice, and

dining room the room in a house where people eat

eyebrow the line of hairs above the eye

want to dance with you.'

'I think I begin to understand,' said Bernice slowly.

'And finally, you'll wake up one morning, knowing you're attractive. And men will know it, too.'

Bernice stood up. 'It's awfully kind of you to help me.'

Marjorie did not answer at first. Then she said dreamily, 'I was just wondering if we should **bob** your hair.'

Bernice gave a scream and fell backwards on to the bed.

The following Wednesday evening there was a dinner-dance at the golf club. At dinner, G. Reece Stoddard was sitting on Bernice's right; he was a good-looking, popular young man. But on her left she only had Charley Paulson, who was short and uninteresting. Remembering Marjorie's teaching, she turned to Charley and said brightly, 'Can I ask you something, Mr Paulson? Do you think I ought to bob my hair?'

Charley smiled and said he didn't know.

'I've decided,' she continued, 'that next week I'm going to the **barber's** to have my hair bobbed.' She noticed that people near her were listening, and she went bravely on, 'Of course, you can all come and watch and I'll sell you tickets.'

People laughed, and G. Reece Stoddard bent towards her and whispered, 'I'll take a ticket right now.' Bernice met his eyes and gave him her most beautiful smile.

'What do you think about bobbed hair?' he asked her quietly.

'I think it's wrong,' she said seriously. 'But you've either got to make people laugh or shock them.' Marjorie had read this somewhere, and made Bernice learn it. 'So I'm going to shock them,' she added.

Two hours later, Warren McIntyre was standing watching the dancers, when he realized something strange was happening. All the boys, led by G. Reece Stoddard and Charley Paulson, wanted to dance with Bernice, who had suddenly become the most popular girl in the room.

bob an old word for 'to have a very short woman's haircut', fashionable in the 1920s for free-thinking women

barber's a shop where people (usually men) have their hair cut; belonging to a man who cuts hair

During the next week Bernice had a wonderful time. She was surrounded by young men, but it was Warren who was always the first to dance with her. Everybody thought that Marjorie didn't mind. But one day she said coldly to her cousin, 'You can forget about Warren. He doesn't like you at all.'

Bernice was surprised, and felt uncomfortable. She hadn't meant to hurt Marjorie or steal Warren from her.

At a party that afternoon, someone started talking again about Bernice having her hair bobbed. Suddenly Marjorie told them all that Bernice was bluffing. People looked at Bernice, expecting her to reply, so she had to say she was ready to do it. In a few moments the whole crowd had driven to the barber's, and Bernice found herself sitting in the barber's chair.

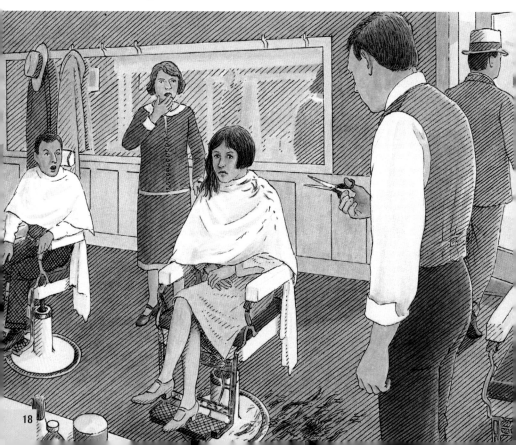

The sharp **scissors** moved fast, and soon her beautiful long dark hair was lying on the ground. She saw in the mirror that all her prettiness had gone. She looked around for Warren, but he had left and was driving Marjorie home.

That evening Mr and Mrs Harvey were deeply shocked to see Bernice's boyishly short hair, and she decided to leave on the next train. When everyone was asleep, she wrote a letter to her aunt, which she left on her bed. She picked up something from a table and walked softly along the hall to Marjorie's room. She went to her sleeping cousin's bedside, picked up Marjorie's long **braids** and cut them both off with her scissors. She returned silently to her own room for her suitcase.

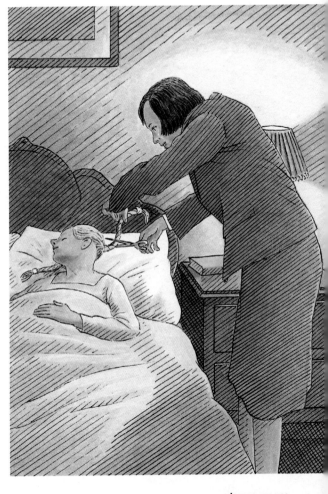

She left the house, feeling strangely happy, and walked towards the station. After a minute, she realized she was still holding the two braids. She laughed unexpectedly, and as she was passing Warren's house, threw the braids at the front door. She laughed again. 'That'll teach her!' she said to herself, before she walked on in the moonlight.

scissors we use these for cutting; they have two long, sharp parts with handles, joined in the middle

braid long hair divided into three parts and twisted together

READING CHECK

Match the first and second parts of these sentences.

a Warren McIntyre loves Marjorie, … ☐ 4

b Marjorie's friends all agree that … ☐

c By chance, Bernice finds out … ☐

d So Bernice decides to … ☐

e Bernice is a fast learner, … ☐

f Marjorie doesn't want Bernice … ☐

g Somehow Bernice finds herself … ☐

h Bernice realizes that having her hair cut … ☐

i Now she wants to make Marjorie … ☐

j So she cuts off Marjorie's braids … ☐

1 sitting in the barber's chair.

2 and becomes very popular with the boys.

3 feel unhappy, too.

4 but she says she doesn't love him.

5 to steal Warren from her.

6 and leaves them outside Warren's door.

7 was a bad idea.

8 accept Marjorie's help.

9 Bernice is no fun to be with.

10 what Marjorie really thinks of her.

WORD WORK

Match the words with the correct pictures on page 21.

a ☐ scissors

b ☐ braid

c ☐ eyebrows

d ☐ dining room

e ☐ barber's

f ☐ country club

g ☐ bob

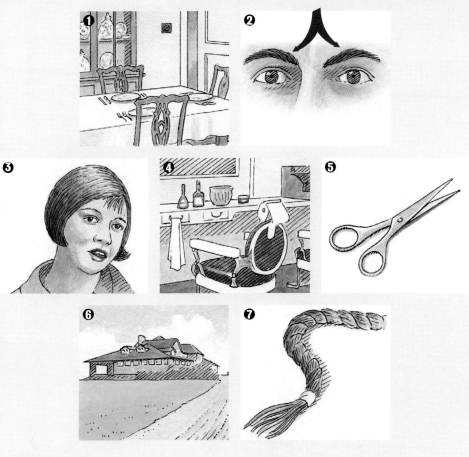

GUESS WHAT

The next story is called *The Cut-glass Bowl*. Match the phrases with the husband and wife in the story.

kind
hard
beautiful
owns a business
spends time with a lover
likes a drink or two
easy to see through

Evylyn Piper

Harold Piper

21

The Cut-glass Bowl

One day a lady called Mrs Fairboalt went to visit her neighbour, the beautiful Mrs Evylyn Piper.

'My *dear*,' said Mrs Fairboalt, 'I *love* your house.'

'I'm so pleased,' replied the beautiful Evylyn. 'You must come here more often. I'm almost *always* alone in the afternoon.'

Mrs Fairboalt was much too polite to say she could not possibly **believe** this. Everyone knew that a young man called Freddy Gedney visited Mrs Piper five afternoons a week.

'I love the dining room most,' she said. 'All those wonderful plates, and that really big **cut-glass** bowl.'

'Oh, there's a story about that bowl,' replied Mrs Piper sweetly. 'You remember young Carleton Canby? At one time he was in love with me, poor boy. When I told him I was going to marry Harold, he stood up very straight and said, "Evylyn, I'm going to give you a wedding present that's as hard as you are and as beautiful and as easy to see through." He frightened me a little – his eyes were so angry! Then that bowl arrived, and of course it's beautiful.'

believe to think that something is true

cut-glass a thick, expensive, heavy glass with deep cuts on one side that catch the light beautifully

'My dear, how very strange!' Mrs Fairboalt was making notes in her head: 'hard, beautiful and easy to see through.' She was looking forward to telling her friends.

As she left the house, she said to herself, **frowning**, 'Some *friend* should speak to Harold Piper. He ought to spend a little *less* time on business, and a little *more* time at home.'

About two minutes later, a good-looking young man rang the front door bell. Mrs Piper, looking surprised, pulled him quickly into the hall.

'I had to see you,' he began wildly. 'Your letter–'

'It's all over, Fred,' said Evylyn. 'Harold knows about us. He's hurt and angry, and he loves me. And – well, I love him too. You've got to leave, Fred. I promised him I wouldn't see you again.'

Freddy was looking miserably at her for the last time, when suddenly they heard a man's footsteps outside. Quickly Evylyn took Freddy's arm and pushed him into the dining room.

'Stay there,' she whispered. 'I'll make him go upstairs, and then you can go out of the front door.'

But when Harold came in, he just wanted to sit in the library, reading his newspaper. Evylyn could not think what to do. 'Perhaps he'll go into the dining room for a drink!' she thought, with **horror**.

Suddenly there was a loud ringing sound from the dining room. Freddy had turned to go out of the back door and his arm had knocked against the cut-glass bowl.

'What's that!' shouted Harold. 'Who's there?'

She tried to stop him, but he broke away. She hurried into the dining room after him, and found him holding Freddy down on the floor. Harold looked up at his wife, with a face full of surprise and then pain. 'You promised, Evylyn! I'll never believe you again!'

She put her arms around him, but he pushed her away. She had never felt so sorry for Harold, or loved him so much.

frown to move your eyebrows down and together when you are serious or angry

horror a feeling of great fear or shock

For several months after this, Evylyn tried to make her husband love her again. But he only laughed angrily, and refused to speak to her. So she too became silent, and a dark shadow came between them. She realized, too late, that she had lost his love for ever.

At thirty-five Evylyn was no longer beautiful, and she knew it. She began to look for women friends, not men. Much of her time was spent with her two children, especially her son, Donald, whom she loved deeply.

One afternoon she was in her bedroom when she heard a sudden scream from downstairs. 'Julie!' she called, recognizing her young daughter's voice.

The **servant**, Hilda, called up the stairs to Evylyn, 'She cut herself a little, Madam.'

Evylyn hurried downstairs and in a moment Julie was in her arms. 'My thumb!' cried Julie. 'Oh, it hurts!'

servant a person who works for someone rich

'It was the bowl in the dining room, Madam,' explained Hilda. 'Julie was playing with it, and it cut her.'

Evylyn washed the blood away and covered the thumb with a clean old **handkerchief**. 'These servants!' she thought in disgust. 'They're useless!' Luckily it was only a small cut, and Julie seemed to be fine.

When Harold came home, he told her he had invited a lot of guests to dinner that evening. One of them was Clarence Ahearn. Harold's business was not doing well, and he hoped Clarence would become his new **partner**, just in time to save his business. 'So it's important for things to go well tonight,' he said. 'Let's make some **punch** in that big cut-glass bowl!'

'Use the small bowl instead,' said Evylyn. 'I don't want a lot of **drunk** men in my house.'

But Harold liked a drink or two himself, and made the punch in the large bowl.

That evening Harold and his cousin Tom both got drunk on the punch, and before anyone could stop him, Tom said some unpleasant things to Clarence Ahearn.

handkerchief something that you use to dry your nose or eyes

partner someone who owns a business with other people

punch a strong, sweet drink, specially made for parties

drunk when someone has had too much strong drink

Just then Evylyn heard Hilda's voice at her elbow. 'Please, madam, Julie's sick. I think it's her hand.'

In a few seconds Evylyn was upstairs at her daughter's bedside, looking in horror at Julie's red and **swollen** hand. '**Blood-poisoning!**' she thought, and ran to the phone to call a doctor immediately.

She could hear loud voices downstairs, and she saw her husband's brother Milton in the hall. 'What's happened?' she called down hurriedly to him.

'There's been a bit of trouble,' he replied. 'Clarence got angry and Harold tried to hit him. They've all left.'

But she had no time to think about her husband. When the doctor came, he said the blood-poisoning was very serious; they would have to **amputate** Julie's swollen hand the next day.

The years passed. There were lines on Evylyn's face, and she frowned most of the time. The young men she had once loved were long forgotten. Now she worried about Harold's failing business, and about Julie, who was thirteen and hated meeting people, because they noticed her missing hand. She also worried about Donald, who had joined the army and was fighting for his country a long way from home.

One evening Hilda came to speak to her. 'I'm sorry, Madam, the postman brought a letter for you today, but I can't remember where I put it. A long narrow letter, it was.'

Together they looked for it, but couldn't find it. Suddenly, in a moment of horror, Evylyn knew where it was. She knew it came from the War Office, and she knew there was death in it.

She sent Hilda away, entered the dining room and walked straight over to the cut-glass bowl. There, inside it, was the letter. She opened the letter, her hands shaking. She read it, then dropped it on the floor. The house was suddenly very quiet.

swollen a lot bigger than usual

blood-poisoning you get this in your body when a dirty cut has gone bad

amputate to cut off a hand or foot

She sat down on the edge of the table and stared at the bowl. It lay there at the centre of her house, never changing, never growing old, a present full of hate from a man whose face she could not remember. She realized that all her married life had been a battle between her and the bowl, a battle she could never win.

It seemed to say to her, 'You know it was I who took your son away. You know how cold I am and how hard and how beautiful, because once you were just as cold and hard and beautiful.'

The light from the cut glass seemed to fill the room. Then there came a voice from far away, like a low, clear bell. 'You see, I am **fate**,' it shouted, 'and stronger than your stupid plans. I am different from your little dreams and I am the passing of time and the end of beauty; all the accidents and mistakes in your life are mine.'

fate the power that some people believe decides everything that happens

effort something that is not easy to do

slip to fall when your feet suddenly move away from under you

The deep sound stopped, and a cold wind blew in from the street. Evylyn knew what she must do. 'I must be quick. I must be strong!' she thought. She put both arms round the heavy bowl, and with a great **effort** lifted it.

Out of the front door she went, and on to the stone steps. There she turned to throw the bowl down. But her fingers were cold and tired and could not let go. In that second she **slipped** and fell forward with a cry, her arms still around the bowl.

The crash was heard at the end of the street. Upstairs a tired man woke up and a young girl cried in her sleep. Moonlight shone on the black figure that lay still at the foot of the steps and on the hundreds of pieces of glass, which were blue, and black edged with yellow, and red edged with black.

READING CHECK

What do they say? Complete the sentences.

1 'I must be quick. I must be strong!'
2 'My thumb! Oh, it hurts!'
3 'I had to see you.'
4 'You see, I am fate.'
5 'I think it's her hand.'
6 'My dear, how very strange!'
7 'I'll never believe you again!'

a ..'My dear, how very strange!'.. Mrs Fairboalt says to Evylyn.
b .... Freddy Gedney tells Evylyn.
c .... Harold says to his wife.
d .... Julie tells her mother.
e .... Hilda informs Evylyn.
f .... the bowl says to Evylyn.
g .... Evylyn tells herself.

WORD WORK

1 **Find words in the glass bowl to complete Evylyn's diary on page 29.**

drunkblood-poisoningpartneramputateswollen
servantpunchcut-glasshandkerchief

What an awful night! Poor little Julie cut her thumb on the **a)** .cut-glass. bowl in the dining room. That stupid **b)** .... of mine let her play with it. I used a clean **c)** .... to tie it up and thought everything was fine. Then Harold told me he'd invited Clarence Ahearn to dinner – he was hoping to make Clarence his new business **d)** .... He made some **e)** .... for the guests in the large bowl, although I told him to use the small one. I was right, of course, because he and his cousin both got **f)** .... I knew that was going to happen. Then Harold got into a fight with Clarence, so I don't think there'll be a new partner in the business now! But the worst thing of all is that Julie's hand is very red and **g)** ...., and she's in pain. I called the doctor as soon as I realized it was serious. He says it's a bad case of **h)** ...., and – this is what's so terrible – tomorrow they will have to **i)** .... her hand!

2 **Correct the boxed words in these sentences. They are all words from _The Cut-glass Bowl_.**

a It's difficult to receive someone who tells lies. ....believe....

b People often down when they are angry. ....

c 'Perhaps he'll find Freddy!' Evylyn thought in hurry . ...

d Some people think that face decides everything that happens to them. ....

e Be careful, don't ship on the icy path! ....

f Evylyn made a great report to lift the bowl. ....

GUESS WHAT

The next story is called _A Short Trip Home_. What do you think happens in it? Circle the words you think are correct.

a Ellen Baker and Eddie Rivers take a trip by _car/train/plane_.

b They meet the ghost of _a young woman/a helpful man/an evil man_ on the way.

c The journey is _Ellen's/Eddie's/the ghost's_ last trip home.

A Short Trip Home

My name's Eddie Rivers, and I'd come home from college for the Christmas holidays. I was in love with Ellen Baker, a beautiful girl I'd known for years, but I wasn't hopeful. Girls of eighteen always prefer older boys, like Joe Jelke and Jim Cathcart.

That night Joe, Jim, Ellen and I were all going to a dance at a hotel. We were picking Ellen up from her parents' home, but Ellen had secretly left the house by the back door. It seemed a strange thing to do, and it made Joe angry; he was crazy about Ellen.

We drove on to the hotel, and there we saw Ellen getting out of a **stranger's** car. The driver of the car was an **evil**-looking, thin-faced man with an unpleasant smile.

'Eddie,' Joe said quietly to me, 'Take Ellen into the hotel, will you? I'm going to have a word with that man.'

I took Ellen inside. Ten minutes later I saw Joe and Jim come in. Joe was very white, with blood on his face.

'He hit Joe with **brass knuckles**,' Jim said in a low, shocked voice. 'Joe was unconscious for a minute or so.'

stranger someone that you don't know

evil very bad

brass knuckles a metal cover that some men put on their fingers to fight with

I found Ellen talking to some friends on the dance floor, and whispered to her what had happened.

'It was Joe's own **fault**,' she said surprisingly. 'I told him not to speak to him.' This wasn't true; she had said nothing.

'But, Ellen, where did you meet him?' I asked.

'On the train,' she answered, adding, 'Stay out of things that aren't your business, Eddie. You see what happened to Joe.'

I looked at her in horror. How could she talk like that? 'But that man's violent!' I cried. 'No girl's safe with him. He used brass knuckles on Joe!'

Her face seemed to harden; when she was thinking of that man, her eyes half closed, shutting out the rest of the world.

She danced with other boys for the rest of the evening, and Joe just sat watching her from the edge of the room.

The next day, I was passing a restaurant when I noticed some men standing outside. One of them called to me, and I turned round. There, looking at me with his evil half-smile, was the thin-faced man. His cold eyes seemed to say, 'Here I am. What are you going to do about it?'

I knew I was quicker with my hands than Joe, so I stepped forward. But suddenly he wasn't there any more.

'Did he go inside?' I asked the other men. They looked at each other. Then one said, 'Who are you talking about?'

Angrily I pushed past them into the restaurant and asked the waiter, 'Where's the man who just walked in here?'

'Didn't see anyone come in,' he said, shaking his head.

Feeling helpless and uncomfortable, I went out.

I drove straight to Ellen's home. Mrs Baker told me Ellen was going to visit some friends, the Brokaws, in Chicago, and was leaving on the 8.30 train that night. I was pleased, because I knew Ellen would be safe there.

fault when it's because of you that something bad happens

I went home and had a long, hot bath. But all the time I was trying to remember something – something in my conversation with Mrs Baker that wasn't right.

Suddenly I sat up in the bath. The Brokaws! I knew Bill Brokaw well. His family weren't in Chicago this Christmas, they were in Florida! I jumped out of the bath, threw my clothes onto my still wet body, and drove like the wind to the station.

I was too late for Ellen's train, but I caught the next one some minutes later. At eight o'clock next morning I arrived in Chicago, jumped off my train, and luckily found her at the station office, writing a lying **telegram** to her mother.

'The Brokaws are in Florida, not Chicago,' I said.

'It was nice of you to travel so far to tell me that.'

'Now you know, why not go on by train to your school?'

'Please leave me alone, Eddie.' Her lovely eyes narrowed and she gave me a **cunning** smile. 'I'm old enough to take care of myself. I *am* going on to school. I've got my ticket east on the five o'clock train. But today I'm going to meet a man.'

'I know who the man is.'

telegram a very short letter that you send very quickly

cunning able to get what you want in a clever way

32

Again the terrible look came back into her eyes and she replied angrily, 'Leave me alone!'

I took the telegram out of her hand and wrote a new one to her mother. Then I said firmly, 'We'll take the five o'clock train east together. But you're going to spend the day with *me*.'

I can only remember parts of that day. We went shopping and Ellen tried to escape by a back door; we drove around in a taxi and I felt sure someone was following us. But at lunch-time she looked me in the eye, straight and honest.

'Eddie, you're my oldest friend. Please **trust** me. If I promise to catch that five o'clock train, will you leave me alone this afternoon? I – I want to say goodbye.'

'Well, I suppose, if you really want to say goodbye–' I looked up suddenly, and saw a look of deep cunning on her face.

We argued all afternoon. In the end I got her into a taxi and we caught the five o'clock train.

In our **compartment** I took her into my arms and said, 'Ellen, you should *trust* me. Tell me all about it.'

'I can't,' she said, very low.

'You met this stranger on the train coming home from school and fell in love with him, isn't that true? He has some kind of **power** over you. He's trying to get something from you. He's not in love with you.'

'What does that matter?'

'It does matter. Instead of trying to fight this thing, you're fighting me. And I love you, Ellen. Do you hear? I love you.'

Suddenly I knew that he was just outside the door, in the **corridor**. She knew it too; the blood left her face and her eyes half closed. I covered her with my coat, hoping she would sleep. I opened the door and went into the corridor.

The man was waiting there. When he saw me, he went into the

trust to believe that someone is honest and good

compartment a small room on a train

power when you can make somebody do what you want

corridor you can walk from compartment to compartment on a train along this

men's smoking-room and I followed him.

'Are you making a **trip** home?' I asked. He was clearly dead. I could see that very well.

'Yes.' With a terrible, soundless laugh he said, 'Get off at Fort Wayne, or I'm going to shoot you.' He showed me the shape of a gun in his pocket.

I shook my head. 'You can't touch me. You see, I know.'

'You get off here or else I'm going to kill you!'

The train stopped at Fort Wayne. We sat staring at each other until the train started moving again.

Then began a slow, powerful, wordless **attack** on me, which lasted five or six hours. A strange, sleepy feeling came over me. I stopped hating him; he was my friend and wanted to help. I should get off the train, *and let him get at Ellen.* With a violent cry, I sat up straight.

'She trusts me. You can't touch her. She's safe!' I said. I noticed a small round hole above his eyebrows, and suddenly I understood. 'You died, or you were killed, near here! And now you're losing your power! Your trip home is over!'

With an evil laugh he moved towards me, and then the room was full of cold air. A door seemed to open behind him, and with a scream he fell to the floor. His body became a shadow, and as I looked more closely, it disappeared.

Some minutes later I returned to the compartment. Ellen's lovely face was white and tired, but she lay in a deep, restful sleep. She was not in his power any more.

Next time I came home from college, I went to the restaurant where I'd seen the stranger. When I described him, one of the customers remembered him.

'That's Joe Varland,' he said. 'He died last year.'

'What did he do? Don't worry, I'm not a policeman, I just want to

trip a journey

attack when you start fighting someone

know. And I'll keep it to myself.'

'Well, he travelled on the trains a lot. He often came here with a lot of money and told us he got it from girls he met on trains. Then he got in a fight one day and a detective shot him.'

I gave the man ten dollars and left. I didn't tell him that part of Joe Varland had made a last trip home.

It's summer now, and I see Ellen almost every day. We talk about everything except that man. Sometimes she stays silent, and I know what she's thinking about.

Of course there are lots of boys in love with her. But things don't look as impossible as they once did. She belongs to me in a way – even if I lose her.

READING CHECK

Tick the correct answers.

a Why is Joe Jelke angry?

1 ☐ He wants to take another girl to the dance.

2 ☑ Ellen has gone to the dance with another boy.

3 ☐ He doesn't like Jim Cathcart.

b What do Ellen's friends think about the thin-faced man?

1 ☐ He's violent, and possibly evil.

2 ☐ He's a very good dancer.

3 ☐ He's interestingly different from them.

c Why does Ellen tell her mother she is visiting friends in Chicago?

1 ☐ She needs to spend some time alone.

2 ☐ The Brokaws have invited her to visit them.

3 ☐ The evil man makes her tell lies.

d Why doesn't the evil man kill Eddie?

1 ☐ The evil man isn't any good at shooting.

2 ☐ Eddie knows the stranger is dead.

3 ☐ The evil man feels bad about killing someone.

e How did the evil man die?

1 ☐ A girl killed him with a knife.

2 ☐ He died in prison.

3 ☐ A detective shot him.

f How does Eddie feel about Ellen now?

1 ☐ He hopes she will love him one day.

2 ☐ He is less interested in her than before.

3 ☐ He is happy because they are engaged.

WORD WORK

Use the words in the train smoke to complete the sentences.

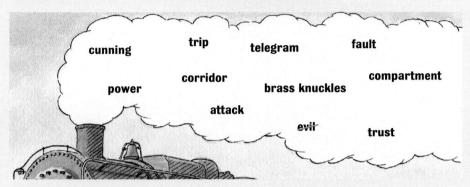

cunning   trip   telegram   fault

corridor   compartment

power   brass knuckles

attack

evil   trust

a Ellen doesn't realize that the thin-faced man is ...... *evil* ....

b The evil man hits Joe Jelke with ....

c Ellen thinks the fight was Joe's ....

d At the station, Ellen is writing a .... to her mother.

e Ellen's smile is .... as she tells another lie.

f Eddie wants Ellen to .... him.

g Eddie and Ellen are sitting in a .... on the train.

h Sadly, Ellen is in the evil man's ....

i The evil man is waiting for Ellen outside in the ....

j The evil man makes a wordless .... on Eddie.

k This is the evil man's last .... home.

GUESS WHAT

The next story is called *Josephine: A Woman with a Past*. What do you think it's about?

a ☐ Josephine killed someone by mistake in the past, and she is afraid that one of her friends will discover this, and that she will go to prison.

b ☐ Josephine has not been a good student and has had many boyfriends before, but she now wants to be more serious and for people to respect her.

c ☐ Josephine is ashamed that her poor family came to America from another country, and she hides this fact from her rich all-American friends.

Josephine: A Woman with a Past

New Haven, home of Yale College, was the city of Josephine Perry's dreams. Twice a year the life-blood of Chicago, where she lived, **flowed** into it, and twice a year it flowed back, when the young men of Yale came home for their Christmas and summer holidays.

But today, seeing it for the first time, she was surprised; the boys they passed didn't look at all attractive. 'I suppose I've been in love too often,' she thought. At seventeen, she had already broken many men's hearts. Now she had only one hope left: the possibility of finding someone she could love more than he loved her.

She and her friend Adele Craw, a nice girl with heavy-looking legs, were in New Haven to buy sports clothes for their school **team**. They found the right shop, and Adele bought what they had come for. A man who was in the shop saw Adele and came forward to talk to her. He was tall, with clear, honest eyes and a kind smile. 'Not my type,' thought Josephine. 'How can he find Adele attractive?' She was introduced to the man, Dudley Knowleton. He spoke politely to her, but she could see that he was interested only in Adele.

'I've got some bad news for you,' he told Adele with a smile. 'You and I will have to start the dancing at the **prom** next week, because I'm president of the prom **committee**. And you know how badly I dance!'

Later, Josephine asked Adele about Dudley. He was in his final year at Yale, a president of several committees and an excellent **baseball** player. Adele had known him all her life, and he was taking her to the prom. They weren't engaged; they were happy to be 'just good friends'.

This was a new idea for Josephine, who believed that boys and girls should be crazy about each other, not 'good friends'. But she found Dudley more attractive now, and hoped he would dance with her at the prom.

flow when something like water moves in one direction

team a number of people who play in a game

prom an important dance at an American school or college

committee a group of people who decide how something should be

baseball a game that lots of people play in America; one person throws a ball and another person hits it with a bat

Josephine had looked forward to the prom for months, but when she saw Dudley and Adele at the head of the dancers, she felt very **disappointed**. She was ten times prettier than Adele, and she had a large crowd of young men wanting to dance with her, but here a girl was only important if the man who brought her was important.

Crossly, she ordered the boy she was dancing with to dance her towards Dudley. Then she gave Dudley her most beautiful smile. He smiled back, and a minute later he asked to dance with her.

'I admire Adele so much, you know,' she said as they danced. 'At school I'm trying to be like her.'

'Are you?' he replied. He was a lot more good-looking than she had once thought.

'I expect boys want to be like you all the time. And of course all the girls fall in love with you.'

'They don't. They never have.'

'Oh, they do, but they're afraid of Adele.'

'Adele wouldn't mind. She doesn't believe in being serious about such things.'

'Neither do I,' agreed Josephine enthusiastically. She was wonderfully happy as she moved round the room in the arms of the president of the prom committee. But in the end another man asked her to dance and she had to accept. She hoped Dudley would ask her again, but by midnight he still hadn't. 'Perhaps Adele's told him about my past,' she thought.

When he finally came up to her, it was to say, 'Adele's got a hole in her **stocking**. Could she borrow a pair from you, as you're staying near here? I can drive you there.'

Josephine agreed happily, and they went together to her house. He waited in the hall as she ran upstairs for the stockings.

'Did you get them?' he asked as she came downstairs.

'Yes. **Kiss** me for being so quick.'

disappointed
unhappy because you don't get what you want

stockings very thin, tight clothes that women wear on their legs and feet

kiss to touch lovingly with your mouth

He laughed lightly, and moved towards the door. She kept on smiling, but secretly she was very disappointed.

'It's been wonderful meeting you,' she said as they drove back. 'I've learnt a lot from you. I used to want to be exciting. Now I want to help people.'

'That's nice.'

Back on the dance floor, she moved in a sweet dream. Then a new man arrived, a tall Southerner, who told her she was the most beautiful girl in the room. After their second dance, he invited her to a friend's flat. It was in the same building, down a corridor and through a door. Inside the flat he took her gently in his arms and kissed her, long and slow. Suddenly they heard a key turn in the lock, a laugh or two, and then the sound of footsteps running away.

'Who was that?' asked Josephine. She noticed they were in a bedroom, not a sitting room.

'Some boy is just playing stupid games. Wait until I get my hands on him! It won't look good if someone on the committee finds us here, will it?'

'We must get out!' Josephine said firmly. She saw a window high up in the wall, and told the man to throw all the blankets from the bed on to the ground outside. He jumped out first, then she followed. She said a quick goodbye to him and returned to the dance floor.

The first person she met was Dudley. 'Sorry I can't stop,' he said. 'There's a man and a girl in a bedroom, and I have to–'

'Could I write to you when I'm back at school?' she broke in. 'I really need a friend I can be serious with.'

'Of course!' He smiled as he hurried away.

As fate had it, she saw him again later. He was helping Adele on with her coat, and explaining, 'The door was locked, and the window open–' Josephine turned away, sure that he and Adele knew *she* was the girl in the flat. But Adele saw her and called to her, 'You were so sweet about the stockings!' She gave Josephine a kiss and said to Dudley, 'Here's a girl you won't find doing bad things. You'll see I'm right: next year she'll be the most **respected** girl in school!'

That spring, Josephine found her ideas were changing. A year ago she wanted fun and dancing and twenty boys in love with her. Now she was beginning to think life was more serious than that. She had read in a book somewhere: 'He is the kind of man who could be the father of my children'. That was surely more important than stolen kisses behind a half-closed door.

Dudley had sent her two letters, which were answers to hers, and she kept them next to her heart. The writer said his baseball team was visiting the town of Hot Springs at Easter, and looked forward to seeing her soon. It was hard to read any feeling into these letters, but Josephine knew every word by heart.

At school, fate was working against her. Some of her friends were caught by a teacher while they were having secret night-time conversations through their bedroom windows with boys. Josephine was **accused** of the crime, along with her friends, and although she explained that she had nothing to do with it, the teachers didn't believe her. She became wildly angry, and forgot to

respect to think that someone is very good

accuse to say that someone has done something bad

be polite and respectful. So she was sent home from school.

Her parents took her to Hot Springs for Easter, and at a dance in the hotel she realized the Yale baseball team was there. Suddenly Dudley was at her side, asking her to dance. He seemed really pleased to see her. She was surprised, and so happy.

'Did – did you hear about what happened at my school?'

'I did. But everybody knows you did nothing wrong.'

'I hoped I'd meet you here. You see, when I really like a boy, I want to be with him all day and all evening. Don't you?'

Dudley was silent for a moment. 'Well, you know, I'm going to be busy – I mean, Adele's getting here tomorrow.'

Josephine felt suddenly frightened. 'You – you'll be with Adele. You were just sorry for me. You like her much better. I'm not your kind of girl, am I?'

'It isn't that,' he said, helplessly.

'Yes, it is,' she replied with feeling, crying miserably. 'I'm just paying for my past.'

He left her, and when she looked round for him he had gone. 'He doesn't love me, so I can forget him,' she thought. 'But I'll never forget what I've learned from him. There are two kinds of men, the ones you play with and the ones you marry.' Her eyes searched the dance floor. She noticed the nice boy who had asked for the first dance that evening; she knew without thinking which kind of man he was. So when he asked her to walk into the moonlight, she took his arm and they went out together.

READING CHECK

1 Are these sentences true or false? Tick the boxes.

		True	False
a	Josephine's excited by the idea of New Haven.	☑	☐
b	Josephine wants Dudley to show interest in her.	☐	☐
c	She is happy to see Adele dancing with Dudley.	☐	☐
d	Dudley writes two love letters to Josephine.	☐	☐
e	In the end, she accepts that Dudley doesn't love her.	☐	☐

2 Correct ten more mistakes in this summary of the story.

Josephine meets Dudley in a ~~food~~ *sports* shop, where her friend Adele is buying some footballs.

Josephine can't understand why Dudley hates Adele so much, and from then on Josephine

thinks a lot about him. She dances with him at the prom, and then asks him for a drink.

Later, she finds herself locked in a kitchen with another young man, and has to jump out

of the window. She hopes that Dudley doesn't find out.

When she goes back to school, she realizes that her teachers have changed; now she

wants to find a man to marry, not just a boy to dance with. In Dudley's letters to her, he

says that his football team is visiting a town called Hot Springs soon. Luckily, Josephine's

grandparents decide to take her to Hot Springs for a holiday, so she meets Dudley at a

party there. At first she is happy because he seems so pleased to see her, but then she

suddenly understands that he likes Adele less than her. It is a shock for her, but,

sensibly, she decides to look around for someone else, and walks out into the sunlight

with a new boyfriend.

ACTIVITIES

WORD WORK

Find words in the picture to complete the sentences.

a Many rivers ......flow...... in the end into the sea.

b Dudley plays for a college sports ....

c The sport that Dudley and his friends play is ....

d A................... is a dance at an American school or college.

e Dudley is the president of several .... at his college.

f Josephine feels .... when she sees Adele with Dudley.

g Adele borrows a pair of .... from Josephine.

h Josephine hopes that Dudley will give her a ....

i Josephine's teachers .... her of doing something bad.

j In future, Josephine wants people to .... her.

accusekissflowbaseballrespectdisappointed
promteamstockingscommittees

GUESS WHAT

The next story – *The Wedding Party* – is about a man called Michael Curly. Guess what happens in it. Tick one of the boxes.

Michael …

a ☐ marries the young woman that he has loved for many years.

b ☐ is invited to a wedding, but arrives late.

c ☐ watches his old girlfriend marry another man.

d ☐ meets the young woman that he is going to marry at a wedding.

e ☐ goes to a wedding where another guest is suddenly killed.

The Wedding Party

A little note was waiting for him at the hotel where he was staying. It contained the usual polite lie: 'I wanted you to be the first to know.' Michael Curly was badly shocked. Caroline was engaged, and was going to be married in two weeks' time! The worst of it was that she wasn't going to get married far away in New York, but right here in Paris, where he lived.

He had met Caroline Dandy in New York when she was seventeen, and they had fallen in love. Then he had lost her, slowly, sadly, uselessly, because he had no money and could make no money. He had no idea what to work at, and although Caroline still loved him, she no longer believed in him.

Broken-hearted, Michael moved to France, but he could not stop thinking of Caroline. Now her note informed him that he had lost her forever.

As he walked in the sunshine down the Rue de Castiglione, he suddenly heard a voice he recognized and his stomach went cold. Turning quickly, he was face to face with Caroline and her **fiancé**.

'Michael! I've been looking for you all over Paris!'

'Why don't they just go away?' Michael thought.

'This is Hamilton Rutherford, my fiancé.'

fiancé the man that a woman is going to marry

It was all very painful. Michael had heard about Hamilton Rutherford. He had bought a business for a hundred and twenty-five thousand dollars of borrowed money and sold it at just the right time for more than half a million. He was not good-looking like Michael, but attractive, **confident**, and taller than Caroline. Michael had always been too short for her when they danced together.

Rutherford was saying, 'Can you come to my **bachelor dinner**? I'd like that very much.'

'And Michael,' added Caroline, 'please come to George Packman's party the day after tomorrow. All my family are here for the wedding.'

All her family – they had always hated him. He felt very small in this game of families and money. Quickly he began to say something about going away.

Then it happened – Caroline saw deep into him, and Michael knew that she saw. All the unforgettable power of first love flowed through both of them again. She took her fiancé's arm suddenly, and said goodbye to Michael.

He walked fast for a minute, then turned to look back at them. 'She'll never be happy, married to him, and I'll never be happy at all any more,' he said to himself.

At his hotel, the **concierge** gave him a telegram, which Michael read. The news was that his grandfather had died, leaving Michael a quarter of a million dollars.

At first Michael was excited, but soon he became miserable again. 'Too late by a single month!' he thought. As he lay awake that night, he could still see the look in Caroline's eyes that morning, a look that seemed to say, 'Oh, why weren't you stronger, why didn't you *make* me marry you?'

He sat up in bed. 'I won't **give up**!' he whispered. 'Even if I can't have her, I can make sure she keeps some of me in her heart.'

confident sure of yourself

bachelor dinner a dinner that a man gives his men friends before he marries

concierge /NAm Eng kɔːnˈsjerz BrEng ˈkɒnsieəʒ/ a person in a French hotel who gives letters or information to people staying there

give up (*past* gave up, given up) to stop trying to do something

So he went to George Packman's party two days later, and met Hamilton's friends, who were all rich, well-dressed and confident. He thought Caroline looked white and tired. One of the guests told him about a surprise some of them were planning for Hamilton's bachelor dinner. They were going to pay a pretty French girl to arrive with a baby in her arms; the girl was going to cry, 'Hamilton, you can't leave me now!' Michael didn't find this at all amusing. Another guest told him that Hamilton was losing money on the **stock market**.

Michael asked Caroline to dance.

'I'm so pleased you came,' she said. 'Now we can be just good friends. I want you and Hamilton to like each other.'

'I've never heard her say stupid things like that before,' thought Michael. Aloud he said pleasantly, 'I could kill him without a moment's worry, but he seems a good man. What I want to know is, what happens to people like me who can't forget?'

She was silent. Then, with a lovely smile, she said, 'I told Hamilton that I'd loved you, but it didn't worry him, because I don't love you any more. And you'll wake up one sunny morning and find you don't love *me* any more, just like that.'

stock market
where people buy and sell shares in companies

Michael shook his head.

'Oh yes, you will. We weren't right for each other. I need someone like Hamilton to decide things for me. It was *that* more than the question – of – of–'

'Of money,' he said. 'Then what about the other day, when we were one person again, with the same heart and blood?'

'Oh don't!' she cried. 'You mustn't talk like that. I love Hamilton with all my heart.'

Michael left the party soon afterwards.

He saw her several times in the next week, but she was always with her fiancé. Michael decided to speak to Hamilton alone, and they agreed to meet in a bar in two days' time. The wedding was now only six days away.

Michael planned what he was going to say: 'See here, Rutherford, do you realize what you're doing? Caroline loves *me*, and now that I have enough money to marry her, we must let her choose between us.' He was fighting for his life.

But when they met, it wasn't a successful conversation. Michael could not **persuade** Hamilton to let Caroline go.

The bachelor dinner took place two days later. Michael put on an expensive new suit, and was surprised to find what a difference it made – he felt much more confident.

Hamilton's friends were ready to bring in the girl with the baby, when another girl arrived unexpectedly to see Hamilton and make trouble for him. Michael went to warn Hamilton, and then, feeling almost hopeful, took a taxi to Caroline's hotel. 'My place is beside her now,' he thought. 'I must be with her when her world comes crashing down around her.'

Caroline came down from her room to meet him in the hall. 'Tell me about your plans, Michael,' she said politely.

persuade to make somebody change their way of thinking

'My plans? The only real plan I ever had was to love you. And now, when I think of all the years ahead without you, without any hope, I don't want to live, Caroline **darling**.'

She was crying softly. 'Poor Michael!' Her hand reached out and touched his chest. 'Why, you've got a new suit!' she said, suddenly smiling. 'Have you **inherited** some money?'

'Yes, a quarter of a million dollars.'

'I'm so happy for you, Michael.'

'Well, it's come just too late to make a difference.'

Hamilton came into the hotel, looking tired. He kissed Caroline and said hello to Michael.

'There was a girl at the dinner, trying to **blackmail** me,' he told Caroline. 'The police are taking care of it now.' He opened two telegrams which Caroline had handed to him. 'Ah, this will interest you,' he said to Michael. 'I've lost every cent I had on the stock market. And I hear *you've* inherited a nice lot of money. Well, that's the way it goes.' He turned to Caroline. 'You understand what I'm saying, darling? I have nothing left.'

Two pairs of eyes watched Caroline for a few moments. Suddenly she stood up and threw herself into Hamilton's arms.

'Oh darling,' she cried, 'I like it better, honestly I do!'

'All right, baby,' said Rutherford. 'Now you get some sleep. I promised to go back to the party for an hour.'

'I'll go with you,' said Michael.

At the wedding Michael, white and shaky after a sleepless night, stood at the back of the church. It seemed to go on for a long time, and then Rutherford and Caroline were walking past him as husband and wife. The guests all moved on to an expensive hotel, and Michael was surprised to discover that even the drinks in the bar were paid for by Hamilton.

'Can you believe it?' George Packman said to him. 'This party

darling
something that you say to someone you love

inherit to receive money from someone when they die

blackmail to ask somebody for money to stop you telling a secret about them

will cost Hamilton five thousand dollars, but he refused to do it more cheaply. I hear he was offered a job at fifty thousand dollars a year, ten minutes before the wedding. He'll be rich again in a few months.'

There was a long, beautifully cooked meal, and there was dancing. Suddenly Michael realized with a shock that he hadn't really thought of Caroline for hours. He saw her across the room, very bright and young and happy, and he saw Rutherford near her, looking lovingly at her. And as he watched them, they seemed to disappear into a world of their own.

cure to make an ill person better

bridesmaid a young woman or girl who helps a woman who is getting married on her wedding day

Michael was **cured**. All his bitterness left him. He was trying to remember which of the **bridesmaids** he had asked to dinner that night, as he stepped forward to say goodbye to Hamilton and Caroline Rutherford.

READING CHECK

Circle the words to complete these sentences.

a Caroline sends Michael *a long letter / a short telegram / (a little note.)*

b Caroline is going to get married in *Paris / London / New York.*

c Hamilton Rutherford is a *teacher / farmer / businessman.*

d Hamilton is *shorter / richer / quieter* than Michael.

e Michael's *grandfather / father / mother* leaves him $250,000.

f Michael thinks the money has come *too late / just in time / too early.*

g Caroline knows that Michael still *hates her / likes Hamilton / loves her.*

h Michael asks Hamilton to *lend him some money / invite him to a party / let Caroline go.*

i Caroline learns that Michael has *inherited money / found a girlfriend / got a job.*

j She chooses to marry Hamilton, although he is *seriously ill / a criminal / very poor.*

k At the wedding, Michael realizes he has fallen *asleep at the table / out of love with Caroline / down the stairs.*

WORD WORK

Complete the sentences with the pairs of words or phrases from the box.

fiancé / confident   bachelor dinner / blackmail   cured / bridesmaid

darling / persuade   concierge / inherited   stock market / gives up

a Caroline's ....*fiancé*...., Hamilton
Rutherford, is a very .*confident*. person.

b The .... at the hotel gives
Michael a telegram which tells him he has
.... a lot of money.

c 'Oh ...., you know how much I love you!' Michael tells Caroline, hoping to .... her to leave Hamilton.

d At Hamilton's ...., a girl tries to .... him by accusing him of being her lover.

e Even when Hamilton loses all his money on the ...., he never ...., and perhaps that's one of the reasons why Caroline loves him.

f At last, Michael knows he is .... of his love for Caroline, and he invites a .... out to dinner.

GUESS WHAT

The next story is about a diamond as big as the Ritz hotel. What do you think happens at the beginning of the story? Tick three boxes.

The diamond ...

a ☐ is kept a secret.

b ☐ is destroyed.

c ☐ brings down the price of all diamonds.

d ☐ brings death to people who know of it.

e ☐ becomes world-famous.

The Diamond as Big as the Ritz

John T. Unger came from Hades, a small town on the Mississippi River. At the age of sixteen he was sent to St Midas's School near Boston, one of the most expensive schools in the world. He enjoyed his time there. The fathers of all the boys were very rich, and John spent the summer staying with schoolfriends. When he told their fathers where he came from (Hades being another name for **hell**), they all said, smiling, 'Is it hot enough for you there?' He was **proud** of his home town, and hated them laughing at it.

In his second year, a boy called Percy Washington came to St Midas's. The only person he made friends with was John, but he said nothing about his family, even to him. So when Percy invited him to spend the summer at his home 'in the West', John accepted at once. He wanted to find out more about his new friend.

It was only when they were in the train that Percy began to talk about his family. He suddenly said, 'My father is by far the richest man in the world.'

'Oh,' said John politely. 'I like very rich people. I visited the Schnlitzer-Murphys last summer, and they had **diamonds** as big as golf balls—'

'That's nothing,' Percy dropped his voice to a whisper. 'My father has a diamond as big as the Ritz Hotel.'

At seven o'clock in the evening they arrived at a small station, where a carriage was waiting for them. After driving for half an hour in the carriage, they stopped next to the largest, most beautiful car John had ever seen. It was made of a shiny metal like silver, and its wheels were covered in **jewels**. Two servants put the boys' luggage in the car.

'Get in,' said Percy to his friend. 'Sorry we had to use the carriage, but we can't let people at the station see this car.'

hell the hot place where some people think that bad people go when they die

proud very happy about something that you have

diamond a very expensive stone that usually has no colour

jewel an expensive stone

They drove uphill through the mountains for some time. Then the car stopped, and the servants got out to put thick **cables** round the wheels. Slowly the great car was lifted over the tallest rocks by a machine, and put down gently on the other side.

'Now we're on our own road,' said Percy, 'on a piece of land that nobody knows about. My grandfather paid a lot of money to make sure it's not on any maps. There's only one thing we're afraid of – only one thing that could find us out.'

'What's that?'

'Aeroplanes. We've got six **anti-aircraft guns** to take care of them, but there have been a few deaths and a lot of prisoners. Father and I don't mind that, of course, but it **upsets** Mother and the girls.'

Suddenly they saw a beautiful **château** in front of them. Moonlight fell on its lake, and there was soft music in the air. The car stopped at the great front door, and Percy said, 'We're home.'

cable a strong, thick, metal rope

anti-aircraft gun a gun that you use to hit enemy planes

upset to make someone unhappy

château /ʃæ'təʊ/ a big, old house or castle where a rich person lives

55

Afterwards John's memories of that first night were **confused**. There were hundreds of rooms in the château, each bigger and brighter than the last. One had walls made of gold, another of diamonds. At dinner, he felt sleepy; the jewels, gold, music, wine and food were making his head go round. He heard a laughing question from Percy's father.

'Yes,' he replied politely, 'it certainly is hot enough for me there.' And then he fell asleep.

When he woke up, he was in the most comfortable bed he had ever known, and Percy was at the bedside.

'I'm sorry,' said John. 'I didn't believe you when you said your family had a diamond as big as the Ritz.'

Percy smiled. 'The château is built on a mountain which is diamond all the way through – one **perfect** diamond.'

At breakfast the next day, Percy explained to John what had happened. His grandfather, Fitz-Norman, had discovered the diamond mountain when he was out riding. He knew he could never sell such a large diamond in one piece, but he didn't want anyone else to find out about it. So he left his younger brother to look after the diamond mountain, and travelled round the world for two years, selling diamonds he had cut from the mountain. When he returned, he was the richest man in the world. But he found he couldn't trust his brother to keep the secret, so he killed him. When he himself died, his son – Percy's father – inherited all the money.

'What a surprising story!' thought John.

After breakfast, he went out into the sunny gardens. Suddenly he saw a girl coming towards him. She was the most beautiful person he had ever seen.

'Hello,' she said softly. 'I'm Kismine.'

She was much more than *just* 'Kismine' to John already. 'You darling,' his eyes said to her.

confused not clear

perfect with nothing wrong

'Are you from the East?' she asked.

'No,' replied John. 'I'm from Hades.'

'I'm going to school in the East after the summer,' she said. 'I like you,' she added in a whisper. 'Are you going to spend all your time with Percy, or will you be nice to me? Just think, I've never had a boy in love with me in all my life. I'm never allowed to see boys alone, except Percy. I came out, hoping to find you here, where the family aren't around.'

John was very pleased, but said nothing.

'I have to go now,' said Kismine sweetly. 'You haven't asked me to kiss you. I thought boys always did that.'

John straightened his back proudly. 'Some of them do,' he replied, 'but not me. Girls don't do that kind of thing in Hades.'

As they walked back to the house together, John's head was full of questions. 'Can I make her fall in love with me?' he was thinking. 'Will I be able to marry her? Will she come back to Hades with me? And how long can her family keep their secret?'

READING CHECK

1 Correct the mistakes in these sentences.

a Hades is a ~~large city~~ *small town* on the Mississippi River.

b At university, John makes a new friend called Percy.

c Percy invites John to stay for a weekend at his home.

d Percy's home is in the east of America.

e Percy and John travel there by boat, horse and carriage, and car.

f You can find Percy's home on a map.

g John remembers almost everything about his first night at Percy's home.

h Percy's grandfather bought the diamond mountain.

i He killed his wife in order to keep the mountain secret.

j John falls in love with Jasmine.

2 Who says this? Who do they say it to? Choose from the names on the right.

a ⑤ 'Is it hot enough for you there?'

b ☐ 'I like very rich people.'

c ☐ 'Sorry we had to use the carriage.'

d ☐ 'I like you.'

e ☐ 'Girls don't do that kind of thing in Hades.'

f ☐ 'Yes, it certainly is hot enough for me there.'

1 Percy to John

2 John to Percy's father

3 Kismine to John

4 John to Percy

5 ~~The fathers of John's schoolfriends to John~~

6 John to Kismine

WORD WORK

Find words in the wordsquare to complete the sentences.

A	C	O	N	F	U	S	E	D
I	C	V	H	G	Z	L	P	I
R	H	B	J	E	Q	H	E	A
C	A	B	L	E	Z	E	R	M
R	T	P	R	O	U	D	F	O
A	E	P	R	A	J	B	E	N
F	A	S	F	J	E	O	C	D
T	U	E	E	S	W	D	T	S
N	F	U	P	S	E	T	L	X
D	T	H	E	L	L	I	G	F

a A .....jewel..... is an expensive stone which is often worn by women.

b That's a .... answer. It has no mistakes in it at all.

c Anti-................. guns are used to attack enemy planes from the ground.

d I didn't mean to .... her. Oh dear, now she's crying!

e Most parents are very .... of their children's successes.

f The students looked .... because they didn't understand their teacher.

g On holiday, we visited a beautiful .... in France.

h A .... can be very useful when you want to pull or lift something heavy.

i Do you think bad people go to .... when they die?

j People sometimes say that .... are a girl's best friend. (This is because the expensive diamonds stay with a woman when the man who gave them leaves!)

GUESS WHAT

Make sentences with these phrases to find out what happens in the next part of the story.

a Kismine falls	**1** plan to	**i** some prisoners.
b Percy's father	**2** he was going	**ii** called Jasmine.
c John meets	**3** shows John	**iii** with John.
d John discovers that	**4** Kismine's sister,	**iv** to die.
e John and Kismine	**5** in love	**v** escape together.

The Diamond as Big as the Ritz

❧ Part 2 ❧

The next day Percy and his father, Braddock Washington, showed John the **golf course**, the farm and the servants' houses.

'Are there many men in the **cage**, Father?' Percy asked suddenly.

Braddock looked angry. 'One got away, you know,' he said. 'I let him out to teach Kismine some Italian, and he escaped! But I hope we've got rid of him. Fourteen of my men in different towns round here reported that they'd each killed a man who looked like the Italian, so maybe one of them got him.'

They had reached a large hole in the ground, covered by strong metal **bars**. Braddock turned on a light, and John looked down into the cage. He saw about twenty men, wearing airmen's uniforms, looking angrily up at Braddock.

'Let us out!' they were shouting. 'You can't keep us here for ever!'

golf course
where people play golf

cage an open box to put animals or people in

bar a strong metal stick that goes across a prison window or door to stop people escaping

'That's where you're wrong,' Braddock replied calmly. 'Be sensible – what else can I do? You've discovered my secret, so I can't let you go. But don't worry, I'll give you food and clothes for the rest of your lives.'

Twenty voices loudly accused Braddock of being the most evil man in the world. But Mr Washington just turned off the light and walked quietly away, followed by the two boys.

It was July, and the weather was very warm. John and Kismine were in love. Late one afternoon, they spent an hour together in the music room. He held her hand and whispered her name. She bent towards him, and then stopped.

'Did you say "Kismine"?' she asked him softly, 'or–' She wanted to be sure she'd heard right.

Neither of them had ever kissed before, but, after an hour or so, that did not seem to matter.

The afternoon passed very pleasantly. That night they each lay awake, happily remembering every minute of the day.

Every day Braddock and the two young men went shooting or fishing in the deep forests, or played golf on the quiet golf course – games which John was careful to let Mr Washington win – or swam in the mountain coolness of the lake.

There was an older sister called Jasmine, who looked a little like Kismine, but had large hands and feet. John realized that Percy and Kismine had probably inherited their **selfishness** from their father, but Jasmine was different: her favourite books were about poor girls who took care of their old parents. But he still loved Kismine, and they planned to marry the following year. John knew he would have to go back to school soon.

Towards the end of August, Kismine said something that deeply shocked John.

selfishness
when you think only about yourself

'Perhaps you're too rich for me to marry you,' he was saying sadly, as they were walking in the garden. 'Perhaps I should marry a businessman's daughter and be happy with her half million.'

'I knew a businessman's daughter once,' said Kismine. 'She was a friend of my sister's. She came to stay here.'

'So you've had other guests?' cried John, surprised.

'Oh yes, a few. But let's talk about something more pleasant.'

'But what's unpleasant about that? Weren't they nice?'

To his great surprise Kismine began to **sob**. 'That's the whole trouble. I really liked some of them. So did Jasmine.'

A dark **suspicion** was born in John's heart.

'Do you mean that they told the family's secret, and your father had them – killed?'

'Worse than that. Father took no chances.' She was sobbing loudly by this time.

John stood there, open-mouthed in horror. 'You mean, he had them killed *before* they left here?'

'Yes, at the end of the summer, after Jasmine and I had had a nice time with them.'

'How terrible! Am I going crazy? Did you just say–'

'Yes, I did. We didn't want to see them shut up in a cage like those airmen. And Father always had it done sooner than we expected, so Jasmine and I didn't have to say goodbye. It was done very nicely. They died in their sleep, you know, so there was no pain.'

'And what about me?' cried John. 'You've let me talk of love to you, and all the time you knew perfectly well I'd never get out of here alive!'

'No,' she **protested**, 'not any more. I did at first. I thought we could *both* enjoy your last few days of life. But then I fell in love with you, and now I'm really sorry you're going to die.'

'Oh, you are, are you?' cried John angrily.

sob to cry sadly, loudly, and suddenly

suspicion a feeling that somebody has done something bad

protest to say strongly that you do not agree with somebody

'Oh, why did I tell you? We were having such fun. I knew it would make things kind of miserable for you.'

Just then, they heard footsteps, and suddenly Braddock Washington was standing in front of them.

'What are you two doing here?' he asked. 'Kismine, go and read a book or play golf with your sister!' He turned and walked away.

'See?' said Kismine crossly. 'We can never meet any more. He'll have you killed if he thinks we're in love.'

'We're not, any more!' cried John wildly. 'And don't think I'm going to stay here any longer. In a few hours I'll be over those mountains and on my way East.'

She put her arm through his. 'I'm going with you.'

'You must be crazy! I'm not taking you!'

'Very well, let's catch Father up and discuss it with him.'

John gave up. He tried to smile at her. 'All right, darling,' he replied, 'we'll go together.'

His love for her returned, and he kissed her. After all, she loved him; she had saved his life by warning him. They decided they would leave the château the next night.

'Will her father find out what we're planning?' wondered John. 'It'll be dangerous – will we be able to escape?'

READING CHECK

1 Put these events from Part 2 of *The Diamond as Big as the Ritz* in the correct order. Number them 1–8.

a ☐ Braddock Washington finds John and Kismine together.

b ☐ John feels angry and argues with Kismine.

c ☐ John and Kismine plan to leave the mountain the next night.

d ☐ John and Kismine make plans to marry.

e ☐ John discovers that the sisters' visitors are always killed.

f ☐ John sees twenty airmen in a hole in the ground.

g ☐ Percy asks about his father's prisoners.

h ☐ John kisses Kismine for the first time.

2 Choose the correct word to complete these sentences.

a Braddock speaks *calmly* / *loudly* / *angrily* to his prisoners.

b That night, Kismine and John lie *sadly* / *happily* / *sensibly* awake remembering their first kiss.

c Jasmine is *prettier* / *richer* / *kinder* than Kismine.

d John is *pleased* / *surprised* / *disappointed* to hear that Kismine has had guests before.

e John hears what happened to the other guests with *horror* / *sadness* / *politeness*.

f Kismine is *happy* / *sorry* / *angry* that she has told John her secret.

g John is *confident* / *careless* / *worried* about their escape plan.

WORD WORK

Use the words from the puzzle to complete the sentences on page 65.

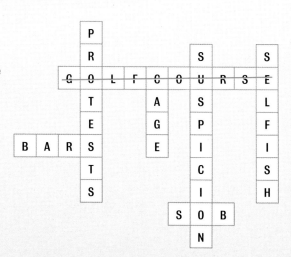

a Percy's father has his own .golf. course. .

b The prisoners are kept in an underground ....

c Percy and Kismine are both more .... than their sister Jasmine.

d Kismine .... that John has the wrong idea about her.

e The airmen can't break the strong metal .... above
their heads.

f John has a .... that unpleasant things have happened.

g Kismine begins to .... as she thinks of her friends who are dead.

GUESS WHAT

What happens in the last part of the story? Tick the boxes.

	Yes	No	Perhaps
a Braddock discovers the escape plan and kills John.	☐	☐	☐
b Planes come to attack the château.	☐	☐	☐
c Percy and both his parents escape.	☐	☐	☐
d The diamond mountain is destroyed.	☐	☐	☐
e Kismine, Jasmine and John set off on their journey to Hades.	☐	☐	☐

The Diamond as Big as the Ritz

❧ Part 3 ❧

That night John was woken by the sound of planes. He sat up suddenly, and heard something else – a footstep and a whisper in the corridor outside his bedroom. Frightened, he jumped out of bed and ran into his bathroom, and from there out into the corridor further along. It was dark, but he could see the shapes of three big men outside his bedroom door. 'They must be the **professional** killers that Mr Washington uses!' he thought. Luckily they did not see him at his bathroom door.

Then he looked past them towards the lift, and saw Braddock Washington standing in it. 'Get in here! All three of you! Now!' shouted Braddock, and the men ran to enter the lift. The doors closed, and the lift went up.

'This is my chance to find Kismine and escape!' thought John. He got dressed quickly and hurried to Kismine's room.

She was standing near the window as he came in. 'Oh, it's you!' she whispered. 'Did you hear them?'

'I heard your father's men looking for me–'

'No, no, the aeroplanes! That Italian who got away – I suppose he told the **authorities**. They've sent their planes to find us. Our anti-aircraft guns are going to start shooting any minute. Let's go up to the roof garden and watch it from there!'

She took his hand and they went out to the lift. As it went upwards, John kissed her. At last he was having an adventure!

A moment later, they were in the roof garden, in the moonlight. Above their heads twelve planes flew in and out of the clouds. From the valley below there were **flashes** of fire as the anti-aircraft guns started shooting. Then the planes began to drop bombs on the gunners below them.

'How exciting!' cried Kismine. 'Look, look!'

professional
doing something as a job for money

authorities the people who control part, or all, of a country

flash a sudden bright light

'We've got to leave before they start to bomb the château!' cried John. 'Come on!'

'Oh, all right,' replied Kismine, who was enjoying the show. 'But we must wake Jasmine and take her with us.' Then she added, with childish happiness, 'We'll be poor, won't we? Like people in books. My parents will be dead so I'll be completely free. Free and poor! What fun!'

'It's impossible to be both free *and* poor,' said John. 'I'd choose to be free myself. I think you should put what you've got in your jewel box into your pockets before we leave.'

Ten minutes later, John and the two girls left the château by a back door. They followed a narrow **path** which went up the diamond mountain.

'I know a place in the woods,' said Kismine, 'halfway up, where we can hide and watch the bombing. Then there's a secret path that we can use to make our escape.'

When they reached the place, they all sat down, and Jasmine fell asleep at once. John and Kismine watched as the planes came closer to the château. Then the guns were silent, and Kismine fell asleep too.

Some time later, John heard footsteps on the path they had taken. He waited until the people had gone past the hiding-place, and then followed them uphill. When he heard the footsteps stop, he hid behind a large rock and looked carefully out.

path a narrow road for people to walk on

Braddock Washington was standing out in the open. The sun was coming up in the east, and its brightness made him look small and powerless. He gave an order to the two servants who were with him. Together, with great effort, they managed to lift the very large, beautifully-cut diamond which lay at their feet. Braddock slowly lifted his arms up to the sky.

'You up there!' he called confidently. 'I, Braddock Washington, am asking you to do one small thing for me – to go back in time and make things the same as they were yesterday. It would be so easy for you! And in return, I will give you the greatest diamond in the world. This one here is just a small example. What do you say?'

'He's offering a **bribe** to **God**!' thought John. He stared at the man, whose hair had gone white as he spoke.

After a moment, the sky went dark and the birds stopped singing. The trees were silent and far over the mountain there was the angry sound of **thunder**. That was all.

John saw the planes landing near the lake. He hurried back to the girls, and together they took the secret path leading away from the château. When they turned to look back, they saw Percy and his mother join Braddock on the mountain. One of the servants opened a door in the ground, and they all climbed inside.

'It must be an underground way out!' thought John.

bribe something expensive that you offer someone to make them do something for you

God an important being who never dies and who decides what happens in the world

thunder a loud noise in the sky when there is a storm

Suddenly both girls screamed as the mountain exploded with a great bang and a flash of bright light. At the same time, the château seemed to throw itself into the air, and then fall in millions of pieces into the lake. After a few moments there was no more noise, and John and the girls were alone.

After a day's walk, they reached the steep mountain which stood between the Washingtons' land and the rest of the world.

'Now,' said John enthusiastically, 'let's see what jewels you brought with you. If you chose well, we three can live comfortably all the rest of our lives.'

But Kismine said with a laugh, 'Oh, how stupid of me! I opened the wrong box, and I've only brought **rhinestones**! But I think I like them better. I'm a little tired of diamonds.'

'Well,' said John sadly. 'We'll have to live in Hades.'

They lay down to sleep for the night.

'What a dream it was,' said Kismine, looking up at the stars. 'And how strange, to be here with one dress and a poor fiancé!'

'Everything's a dream when you're young,' said John quietly. 'Go to sleep now, little girl, and forget about the real world for a while.'

rhinestone a stone with no colour that looks like a diamond but is not expensive

READING CHECK

1 Match the sentences with the people.

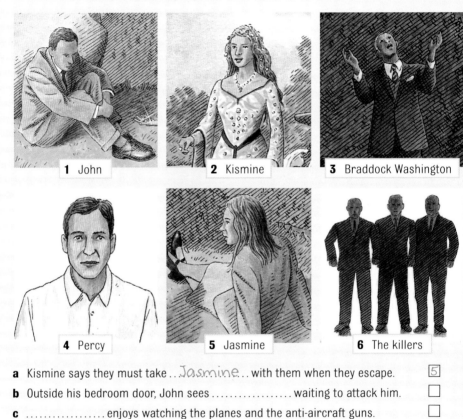

1 John   **2** Kismine   **3** Braddock Washington

4 Percy   **5** Jasmine   **6** The killers

a Kismine says they must take ...Jasmine... with them when they escape.   5

b Outside his bedroom door, John sees .... waiting to attack him. ☐

c .... enjoys watching the planes and the anti-aircraft guns. ☐

d .... wants Kismine to bring some jewels with her. ☐

e On the mountain, ... tries to ask for help. ☐

f .... and his mother both die when the mountain explodes. ☐

2 Match the first and second parts of the sentences.

a 'Get in here! Now!'   **1** John tells Kismine sadly.

b 'Free and poor! What fun!'   **2** shouts Braddock to the killers.

c 'You up there!'   **3** thinks John about the door in the ground.

d 'It must be an underground way out!'   **4** Braddock says, asking God to listen to him.

e 'We'll have to live in Hades,'   **5** Kismine says to John about their new life togethe

ACTIVITIES

WORD WORK

Use the letters in the diamonds to complete the sentences.

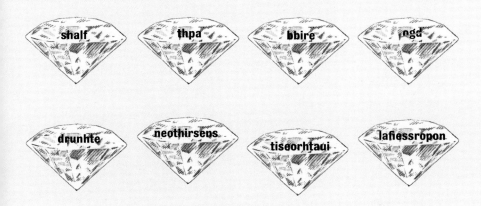

shalf   thpa   bbire   ngd

drunhte   neothirsens   tiseorhtaui   lafiessropon

a Braddock Washington asks G o d to help him.

b Braddock pays p _ _ _ _ _ _ _ _ _ _ _ killers to kill people who find out his secret.

c Braddock thinks that you can b _ _ _ _ anyone to do what you want.

d John hears the sound of t _ _ _ _ _ _ , far away in the sky.

e The a _ _ _ _ _ _ _ _ _ have sent their planes to attack the château.

f There is a bright f _ _ _ _ as the first gun starts shooting at the planes.

g Luckily there is a secret p _ _ _ leading away from the château.

h Kismine has only brought r _ _ _ _ _ _ _ _ _ _ with her, not diamonds.

WHAT NEXT?

1 Have you seen any films of F. Scott Fitzgerald's stories? What were they like?

2 Which of F. Scott Fitzgerald's stories would you like to read next? Why?

This Side of Paradise – a young man's experience of growing up and falling in love.

The Great Gatsby – a rich, mysterious man is secretly in love with a girl called Daisy.

The Last Tycoon – about a film producer in Hollywood.

Tender is the Night – about a man who seems to have a wonderful life, but whose marriage is in deep trouble.

Project A *Playscripts*

1 Read the playscript of a scene from *The Diamond as Big as the Ritz*. Order the dialogue. Start with *a*, and number the lines 1–14.

a ☐ JOHN: Kismine, my darling–

b ☐ KISMINE: Married? Oh, yes, let's! (*They kiss a third time.*)

c ☐ JOHN: You're right. Well, here you are – 'I love you, I love you, I love you!'

d ☐ KISMINE: Did you say Kismine? Or kiss me?

e ☐ JOHN: Well, if I love you and you love me, let's get married! As soon as possible!

f ☐ KISMINE: You're so sweet. And now what do *I* say?

g ☐ JOHN: Well, it's the same for me. I've never kissed a girl before.

h ☐ KISMINE: All right. If I must, I must. I love you too, darling John.

i ☐ JOHN: No, I'm finding it surprisingly easy. (*They kiss a second time.*)

j ☐ KISMINE: That was nice. You know, this is the very first time I've kissed a boy.

k ☐ JOHN: Kiss me, Kismine, my love! (*They kiss.*)

l ☐ KISMINE: It isn't difficult, is it?

m ☐ JOHN: You have to say 'I love you too, darling'.

n ☐ KISMINE: That was even nicer. But I think boys usually say 'I love you' when they kiss a girl.

2 Complete this page of Kismine's diary for the same day, using phrases from the playscript in Activity 1.

What a wonderful day today! John really is **a)** ....
And kissing is **b)** .... – I never realized that, because
of course I've never **c)** .... before. How nice that he
d) .... me, and I **e)** .... him! He wants us to
get **f)** .... and he says that it should be **g)** ....
But I didn't like to tell him that he's going to die soon! Oh dear, how
very sad! Poor **h)** .... John!

3 **Read this page from Michael's diary for the day in *The Wedding Party* when he meets Hamilton and tries to persuade him to give up Caroline.**

> *Hamilton. He thinks a man has to tell his girl what to do. He says you mustn't let her push you around! He just doesn't understand that women have finer feelings than we men do. Caroline has finer feelings. I told him that, but he didn't believe me. He talked about making a good start. But: if Caroline doesn't love him, how can it be a good start? When I asked him that, he said that she does love him. And then, he told me that, in the past, she and I didn't love each other at all, we were only sorry for each other! He thinks that he's just what Caroline wants. I feel miserable.*

Complete Michael's part of this playscript with phrases from his diary.

HAMILTON: You have to tell your girl what's what. Don't let her push you around.

MICHAEL: (*angrily*) But **a)** . . . .

HAMILTON: That's rubbish! They don't.

MICHAEL: (*coldly*) Well, Caroline **b)** . . . .

HAMILTON: That's not true. What *is* true is that she knows me and I know her. It's a good start.

MICHAEL: But **c)** . . . . ?

HAMILTON: She *does* love me. You think you and she loved each other, I suppose?

MICHAEL: Well, **d)** . . . .

HAMILTON: You were just sorry for each other! Luckily, Caroline has what she wants now.

MICHAEL: And what **e)** . . . . ?

HAMILTON: Me. Sorry, I have to go now. See you at the bachelor dinner.

4 **Choose one of these scenes and write a playscript of it.**

Bernice Bobs Her Hair: Marjorie tells her friends Bernice is bluffing about getting her hair cut (pages 14–15)

The Cut-glass Bowl: Carleton Canby gives Evylyn the bowl as a wedding present (page 22)

A Short Trip Home: Joe Jelke faces up to the evil stranger (page 34)

Josephine: A Woman with a Past: Josephine first discusses Dudley with Adele (page 38)

Project B *From death to birth*

1 Read this backwards biography of F. Scott Fitzgerald. Answer questions a–j.

Francis Scott Key Fitzgerald died of a heart attack in December 1940. He was a drinker all his life, and had had heart problems for some time. During his life he wrote four novels, *This Side of Paradise, The Beautiful and Damned, Tender is the Night* and *The Great Gatsby*, and a fifth unfinished one, *The Last Tycoon*, as well as many short stories.

In the 1930s, he spent a lot of time in Hollywood, working on film scripts, short stories and his fifth novel; by now he was separated from his wife Zelda. The most important decade in his life was the 1920s, when his best-known novel *The Great Gatsby* was published (in 1925), and the famous writer Ernest Hemingway was a close friend of his. Although many people had heard of Fitzgerald and read his stories, he always had money problems.

At about this time, Zelda became mentally ill. He and Zelda had married in 1920 after Fitzgerald had published his first novel *This Side of Paradise*, and their only daughter was born in 1921. Fitzgerald had met Zelda Sayre at a country club and they got engaged in 1919. She once broke off the engagement, because she did not think that Fitzgerald could make enough money for them both to live on.

Before meeting Zelda, Fitzgerald joined the US army during World War I, but the war ended soon afterwards. Earlier, Fitzgerald had been a student at Princeton University in New Jersey, where he became friends with future writers and started writing himself. He was born in St Paul, Minnesota, USA, in 1896.

a When did F. Scott Fitzgerald die? ....
b Where did he spend time in the 1930s? ....
c What was his wife's name? ....

d What was the most important time in his life? ....

e What's the name of his best-known novel? ....

f Who was a famous writer friend of his? ....

g What problems did he have in his life? ....

h When did he marry? ....

i Where did he study? ....

j When was he born? ....

2 Complete the questions about Gerald Durrell's life with the words in the box.

| all   and   is   did   ~~die~~   he   in   his   of   to   was   zoo |

a When did he ..die..? January 1995

b When did he marry .... second wife? 1979

c Why did he start his own ....? To save rare animals from disappearing

d Where .... his zoo? Jersey, one of the Channel Islands

e Why did .... write books? To make money for more journeys round the world to study and collect animals

f What's the name .... his most famous book? My Family and Other Animals

g Who .... his first wife? Jacqueline Wolfenden

h Where .... he work during World War II? In a pet shop, then on a farm

i Who was an important person .... his life when he was a boy? Theodore Stephanides

j Where did he live from 1935 .... 1939? The island of Corfu, in Greece

k What was he interested in .... his life? Animals and insects

l Where .... when was he born? In India in 1925

3 Complete the backwards biography of Gerald Durrell, using information from Activity 2 on page 75.

Gerald Malcolm Durrell died in **a)** ...., after an operation to give him a new liver. His hard outdoors life had brought him health problems in the 1980s. He was a writer, a zookeeper, and a TV presenter, and he wrote books about animals and zoos, short stories, novels, and stories for children.

In **b)** .... his first wife divorced him, and he married Lee McGeorge in the same year. He wanted to **c)** ...., so he started his own zoo on **d)** .... in 1958; here he kept the large collection of animals which he had brought together from all round the world. In the 1950s, he published several amusing books about his life, to **e)** ....; his first book *The Overloaded Ark* was a great success, and **f)** .... (1956) became his most famous book.

He married his first wife, **g)** ...., in 1951; she went with him on most of his journeys and helped with his work. From 1946, he went many times to different parts of the world to study and collect animals, and became well known for his work with wild animals. During World War II, he had worked in **h)** ....

Someone who played a very important part in his life when he was a boy was **i)** ...., a friend of Durrell's teacher. Durrell and his family lived on **j)** .... from 1935 to 1939, and together Durrell (as a young boy) and Theodore studied and collected examples of Corfu wildlife. All his life Durrell was deeply interested in **k)** .... and **l)** .... Although he was British, he was born in **m)** ....

4 Choose one of these authors. Research his or her life. Write a backwards biography of your chosen author, starting at death, and ending at birth.

Jack London

Edith Nesbit

O. Henry

Joseph Conrad

GRAMMAR CHECK

Prefixes and suffixes

We use un– to form negative adjectives.

Roger Button buys unsuitable clothes for his son.

We use –ly to form adverbs from adjectives.

Benjamin's heart beats loudly when he sees Hildegarde.

We use –able/–ed/–ful/–less/--looking to form adjectives.

Bernice felt surprised and uncomfortable.

Baby Benjamin is a strange-looking child.

Then began a slow, powerful, wordless attack on me.

Ellen's lovely face was white and tired.

We add –ness/–y to form nouns from adjectives.

At first, people have difficulty in accepting Benjamin.

Benjamin is full of happiness when he gets married.

We use –side to show a place.

Roscoe sometimes comes to his father's bedside.

---

1 **Complete Hildegarde's thoughts about Benjamin with the words in brackets and the prefixes/suffixes in the box. Make necessary spelling changes.**

–able ~~–ed~~ –ful –less --looking –ly –ly –ly	
–ness –side un– –y –y –ful	

That man seems very **a)** .i.n.t.e.r.e.s.t.e.d. (interest) in me. He keeps staring at me.
How **b)** .... (good) he is! I suppose he's about fifty. He looks almost
c) .... (father). I can see **d)** .... (honest) and
e) .... (kind) in his face. It's **f)** .... (notice) how polite
and **g)** .... (thought) he is to all the people around him. I think he's
much nicer than all the stupid boys I **h)** .... (usual) dance with. They
seem so **i)** .... (intelligent)! I **j)** .... (real) hope he'll ask
me to dance. And perhaps, later on, we can take a walk **k)** .... (out).
How **l)** .... (luck) there's a full moon tonight, in a **m)** ....
(cloud) sky – it's a **n)** .... (beauty) evening for talking about love!

GRAMMAR CHECK

Modal auxiliary verbs: ought to and should

We use ought to or should + infinitive when giving advice about what is the right thing to do.

> You ought to think about me sometimes, Marjorie.

(= infinitive with *to*)

> You should accept that I don't love you, Warren.

(= infinitive without *to*)

> Bernice, you shouldn't say things that you don't mean!

> What should I do, Marjorie? Should I go home early?

To make a negative, we usually use shouldn't + infinitive without *to*.

To ask a question, we usually use should + subject + infinitive without *to*.

2 Complete Mrs Harvey's advice to her niece Bernice with *should*, *ought to* or *shouldn't*.

a You ..*shouldn't*.. worry too much about being popular.

b You .... to stay with us a few days longer.

c You .... listen at bedroom doors!

d You .... think of interesting things to say.

e You .... to listen to Marjorie. She can help you.

f You .... even think of having your hair cut!

3 Complete Marjorie's advice to her cousin Bernice with *should*, *ought to* or *shouldn't*.

a You ..... *ought* ..... to brush your eyebrows.

b You .... to have your teeth straightened.

c You .... stand so straight when you dance.

d You .... to wear more fashionable dresses.

e You .... be nice to the 'sad birds'.

f Perhaps you .... even have your hair bobbed.

g And you .... to keep away from Warren.

GRAMMAR CHECK

Past Perfect: affirmative

We use the Past Perfect when we are already talking about the past (using the Past Simple), and we want to talk about an action that happened earlier in the past, before the Past Simple action. To make the Past Perfect, we use had + past participle.

Harold was angry because Freddie had visited Evylyn again.

We put **adverbs** between **had** and the **past participle**.

Harold had already spoken to Evylyn about this a number of times.

We often use relative pronouns – such as *that*, *which*, *who*, and *whom* – to link the Past Simple and Past Perfect.

Evylyn owned a cut-glass bowl that Carleton Canby had given her.

We often use time expressions – such as *by the/this time*, *already*, *earlier*, *all his/her life*, and *by then.* – with the Past Perfect.

By the time Evylyn was thirty-five, she had lost all her beauty.

4 Complete the sentences. Use the Past Simple or Past Perfect form of the verbs in brackets.

a Evylyn ..... tried ..... (try) to make Harold love her again, but by then, she had ... broken ... (break) his heart.

b Harold .... (make) punch for the guests whom he .... (invite) to dinner.

c Julie .... (get) blood-poisoning because earlier that day she .... (cut) her hand on the glass bowl.

d A guest .... (become) angry because Harold's cousin Tom .... (say) some unpleasant things to him earlier.

e Now she was older, Evylyn no longer .... (remember) the young men whom she .... (love) once.

f She .... (worry) about Donald, who by this time .... (join) the army and .... (already/leave) home.

g Evylyn .... (realize) that all her married life she .... (fight) against the bowl.

h When Harold .... (come) downstairs, Evylyn .... (already slip) on the steps and .... (die).

GRAMMAR CHECK

Modal auxiliary verbs: must/may/can't

We use **must** + be when we think that something is true.

Ellen doesn't usually lie – she must be in the stranger's power!

We use **can't** + be when we think that something is not true.

The stranger can't be alive – he's the ghost of Joe Varland.

We use **may** + be when we think that perhaps something is true, but we are not sure.

There may be a chance for Eddie to marry Ellen one day.

5 **Complete the conversation between Eddie and Joe at the beginning of the story *A Short Trip Home*. Use *must, may* or *can't*.**

Joe: What's happened to Ellen? We've been waiting a long time for her! It's cold out here in the car!

Eddie: Calm down, Joe! She **a)** ......may...... still be in her room, getting ready.

Joe: She **b)** .... be there. I asked the servants and they say she went out!

Eddie: Then let's drive to the hotel. She **c)** .... be there already. Let's see.

Joe: All right. It's just round the corner. (They drive to the hotel.) Well, here we are. Look, Eddie! See the girl getting out of that car? It **d)** .... be her! Yes, I'm sure it's Ellen!

Eddie: I don't like the look of the man in the driving seat. He **e)** .... be a stranger in town. I'm sure I don't recognize him.

Joe: He **f)** .... be good for her. He looks evil. I'm going to try to get her away from him.

Eddie: Is that a good idea? He **g)** .... be a friend of hers. Who knows?

Joe: Ellen **h)** .... be safe with him. I'm going to save her from him. Hold my hat, Eddie!

Eddie: Be very careful, Joe. He **i)** .... be violent. It's best not to take any chances!

GRAMMAR CHECK

Causative make

We use causative make with make + object + adjective/noun to talk about what something or someone does to somebody.

Dancing usually makes Josephine happy.

We use causative make + object + infinitive without *to* to talk about what someone or something causes to happen.

Dudley makes Josephine understand something important about life.

6 **Complete Josephine's letter to a friend with the correct words from the box.**

> dance   laugh   show   miserable   ~~come~~   cross   look   happy   fall

Dear Lucy,

Well, here I am in New Haven at last, hoping to make my dreams
a) ......come...... true! As you know, I'm still looking for someone who will make
me **b)** .... wildly in love with him. So far, the boys I've seen here
don't even make me **c)** .... at them twice! But today I met someone
called Dudley. He's tall and has wonderful eyes. I tried hard to make him
d) .... an interest in me, but he only seems to like my friend Adele.
She says they aren't even engaged, just good friends! That made me
e) .... and I nearly shouted at her. What a stupid idea!

But guess what, I've got a plan. In a few days' time we'll all be at the prom, and
I'm going to make Dudley **f)** .... with me. Perhaps that will make
Adele **g)** .... and she'll cry a bit. I hope not too much, because she's a
nice girl, and she's my friend. But I know it'll make me very **h)** ....,
being in Dudley's arms!

Don't worry, I'll tell you all about it in my next letter. It'll probably make you
i) .... or cry, I don't know which!

With much love,

Josephine

GRAMMAR

GRAMMAR CHECK

First conditional

We use the first conditional for a possible future action which depends on another action. We use will/won't in the main clause, and the Present Simple in the if clause.

When the if clause comes at the start of the sentence, we put a comma after it.

If Caroline really loves Michael, she'll marry him.

When the if clause comes at the end of the sentence, we don't use a comma.

Perhaps Caroline won't marry Hamilton if he loses all his money.

7 **Complete the thoughts of characters from *The Wedding Party*, using the first conditional. Put the verbs in brackets in the correct form.**

Caroline Dandy: The problem is that if I **a)** ....marry.... (marry) Michael, we **b)** .... (never have) any money. But if I **c)** .... (choose) Hamilton, he **d)** .... (take care) of me. I think I know what to do!

Concierge: If Mr Curly **e)** .... (receive) good news in that telegram, perhaps he **f)** .... (give) me some money! I think he **g)** .... (have) more luck with women if he **h)** .... (spend) more money on his clothes. He's a nice young man. I hope he finds love.

Michael Curly: If she **i)** .... (marry) Hamilton, she **j)** .... (be) unhappy for ever! But I'm too poor to marry her now. There's one thing I'm sure of – I **k)** .... (ask) her to marry me if I **l)** .... (inherit) some money.

Hamilton Rutherford: Caroline **m)** .... (not have) a chance of happiness if she **n)** .... (accept) Michael. I hope she doesn't say yes to him. If she and I **o)** .... (get married), I **p)** .... (do) my best to make her happy.

George Packman: I **q)** .... (lend) Hamilton some money if he **r)** .... (can not) pay for the wedding. After all, he's my oldest friend. But I think he **s)** .... (be) rich again soon if he **t)** .... (take) that job!

GRAMMAR CHECK

Causative have

We use causative have when someone asks somebody to do something for them.

The Washingtons have their guests driven from the station to the château.

We use have + object + the past participle form of the verb, in that order.

Mrs Washington has all the housework done for her.

We put by + the person after the past participle to say who does the action.

John has his letters to Hades posted by a servant.

8 Order these jumbled sentences about *The Diamond as Big as the Ritz*.

a car Percy father's rocks the lifted his has over

.....Percy has his father's car lifted over the rocks.....

b prisoners has in Braddock a cage twenty kept

....

c château six guns to has Braddock anti-aircraft the brought

....

d large killed of men has a Braddock number

....

e The cleaned them Washingtons château their for have

....

f Washington all Mrs the cooked servants has meals by

....

g Jasmine clothes her for has washed her

....

h hair Kismine has done her her for

....

i his Percy a cleaned has by shoes servant

....

j him for John made bed his has

....

k visitors killed his Braddock always family's has

....

DOMINOES Your Choice

Read *Dominoes* for pleasure, or to develop language skills. It's your choice.

Each *Domino* reader includes:
- a good story to enjoy
- integrated activities to develop reading skills and increase vocabulary
- task-based projects – perfect for CEFR portfolios
- contextualized grammar activities

Each *Domino* pack contains a reader, and an excitingly dramatized audio recording of the story

If you liked this *Domino*, read these:

Mansfield Park
Jane Austen

'Why shouldn't we offer to take care of her? She could live with us at Mansfield.'

In this way Mrs Norris persuades her sister, Lady Bertram, and Lady Bertram's husband, Sir Thomas, to ask their poor niece Fanny Price to live with them at Mansfield Park.

At first, Fanny is unhappy there. Then, after she makes friends with her young cousins, things improve. But what happens when the cousins are older, and starting to think of love?

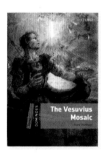

The Vesuvius Mosaic
Joyce Hannam

'We have some wonderful mosaics in Pompeii, but I've never seen a better one than this!'

After the young Roman mosaic designer Felix starts work in Pompeii, his whole life changes. There he falls in love with the beautiful Greek slave Agathe, who can see into the future.

When the volcano Vesuvius sends hot ash over the city, Felix – and Agathe's brother Alcander – ride to the port of Misenum for help. But will they reach admiral Gaius Plinius in time, and will they ever see Agathe alive again?

	CEFR	Cambridge Exams	IELTS	TOEFL iBT	TOEIC
Level 3	B1	PET	4.0	57-86	550
Level 2	A2–B1	KET-PET	3.0-4.0	–	390
Level 1	A1–A2	YLE Flyers/KET	3.0	–	225
Starter & Quick Starter	A1	YLE Movers	1.0–2.0	–	–

You can find details and a full list of books and teachers' resources on our website:
www.oup.com/elt/gradedreaders